GLASS
PAPERWEIGHTS
OF THE
NEW-YORK HISTORICAL SOCIETY

Books by Paul Hollister

THE ENCYCLOPEDIA OF GLASS PAPERWEIGHTS
GLASS PAPERWEIGHTS OF THE NEW-YORK HISTORICAL SOCIETY

GLASS
PAPERWEIGHTS
OF THE
NEW-YORK HISTORICAL SOCIETY

BY PAUL HOLLISTER
PHOTOGRAPHS BY H. LANDSHOFF
FOREWORD BY MARY BLACK

Clarkson N. Potter, Inc./Publisher
NEW YORK

DISTRIBUTED BY CROWN PUBLISHERS, INC.

FOR
Irene and Mary

CONTENTS

FOREWORD

MANY PEOPLE ALREADY KNOW THE BEAUTY AND PLEASURE OF GLASS PAPERWEIGHTS. Most of these objects are small—a cool, smooth, glassy handful in which lies a garden of flowers, a single blossom, or a butterfly. The design in each paperweight is ordered and magnified by the clear glass that forms its protective covering and shell.

Nineteenth-century American and European glass paperweights appeal not only to the senses of touch and sight, but also to the imagination. Seeing weights as miniature planets is not too farfetched an image; somehow ownership of even one gives the possessor a sense of being in command of a mysterious, systematic, and altogether perfect unit of a tiny universe.

The fact that paperweights are small has meant that they were once popular gifts, both inexpensive and beautiful, and easily transported by pocket or hand luggage. Added to this is the charm of the designs that lie within; interior gardens or creatures that remain forever in the state of order in which they were created. It is small wonder that paperweights continue to be prized today and that the value of these once inexpensive novelties increases every year.

While the general shape of glass paperweights follows a prescribed form, the tiny objects encased within vary greatly in design and in the way in which they are assembled. The variety and richness of these combinations of wafer slices or fused elements of glass can scarcely be imagined. Occasionally, as Paul Hollister notes, one may find slices from the same cane in more than one weight. While groups of weights from the same factory may present uniformity of outline and near uniformity of interior arrangement, individuality occurs in the selection and in the combinations of elements within each weight. It is the discovery of the often infinitesimal differences that so delights the collector.

Over a period of years Paul Hollister has come to be one of, if not the, leading authority on glass paperweights. His knowledge has been acquired through the study of related literature on glassmaking, through observation of the methods of modern glassworkers, and, most importantly, through lengthy and intensive study of thousands of paperweights. This background of information and his broad knowledge of weights from many factories throughout thier history allows him to analyze the grand collection in the New-York Historical Society and come to highly informed conclusions as to the place, date, and maker of each piece.

Mr. Hollister, who is an artist with fourteen one-man shows to his credit, sees paperweights with a painter's eye; this point of view fortifies his technical knowledge of weight making and led to his initial investigation of these objects. Mr. Hollister's first cataloging assignment in this field was for Old Sturbridge Village. (The fine collection of paperweights at that museum was given to the Village by J. Cheney Wells, Mr. Hollister's stepfather.) In more recent years he has cataloged and appraised numerous paperweight collections for museums and private collectors. Sometimes he did this work without charge in order to learn more about paperweight structure and in exchange for permission to photograph these collections in color. In this way he first became familiar with the paperweights in the Society's collection. The discovery and search for information on glass paperweights soon developed into an interest that consumed much of Mr. Hollister's working and leisure hours.

About 1971 a number of cooperating forces came together to make this book possible. A large part of the Society's collection was soon to be sent on tour in an exhibition that would stop at five museums in New York State. Before it left, however, we wished to record its treasures, and the idea of a published catalog of the collection came into being. A publisher was found; Paul Hollister agreed to write the catalog, to outline his knowledge of the history of paperweight making, and to arrange the weights for photographs.

For the pictorial record the services of H. Landshoff were secured. Mr. Landshoff is well known for his photographs, particularly those he did for *The Shell,* by Hugh and Marguerite Stix and R. Tucker Abbott, and for *The Doll,* by Carl Fox. The photography of paperweights was a project ideally suited to this skilled man, a meticulous workman who brings an artist's sensibilities to his work. It was a task carried out with a technician's concern for accuracy.

For many weeks the work went on in a small gallery in which the paperweights had recently been installed. The gallery was closed to the public, and Mr. Hollister and Mr. Landshoff worked around a white plastic-topped table that they had set up as the ideal background for recording the groups of paperweights. Nothing was left to chance: the arrangements of comparable weights were designed by Paul Hollister, plate by plate. Each of the 120 color plates illustrates weights of similar types from various factories so as to show the range of production. It is the first published across-the-board survey of glass paperweights.

The decisions concerning arrangements gave Mr. Hollister yet another opportunity to review the composition of each weight, and to recheck attributions and condition in record notations for the Society and for students. For this curator, an observer rather than a participant, it was an experience in learning to see and appreciate the care being spent in extending knowledge of these small beautiful objects.

This book sets a precedent for paperweight classification in many respects: the overall collection is one of the largest in a public museum and comprises a wide variety of the finest weights from what Mr. Hollister terms the Classic Period of manufacture (from 1845 to 1855) and from subsequent revivals of production into the early twentieth century. In the section in which the color plates are discussed Paul Hollister describes the salient features of some 400 paperweights with information and insights that only an expert would have. For the first time in a catalog of paperweights a description of the construction of these mysterious enclosed glass flowers and fruits is attempted, and Mr. Hollister further notes the present condition of the weights in this collection. The observant reader and viewer now may note how the characteristic overall shape of some weights may have been altered from the original by regrinding.

In many ways this volume, besides being an armchair guide to the Society's collection, is a survey of mid-nineteenth century to early twentieth-century paperweight production, country by country, including all the leading factories. The plates and their accompanying descriptions range from the commonest types to those both elaborate and rare. Mr. Hollister also offers informed, common sense advice to the collector.

The publication of the catalog of paperweights in the Society's collection has been carried to completion by Clarkson Potter, and it is a pleasure to acknowledge our appreciation for his undertaking of this task. The form of the book was outlined by Paul Hollister in his arrangement of weights, but all of us concerned are grateful to Ruth Smerechniak for her design, to Jane West as senior editor, and to Diane Girling, as production editor.

A single paperweight may be a source of great pleasure merely as a beautiful object. But this compendium of many designs seeks to make these objects more than beautiful—to give the reader an appreciation of their style and the methods of their manufacture.

—MARY BLACK

The Glass Paperweight Collections
of the New-York Historical Society

THE FIRST OF THE NEW-YORK HISTORICAL SOCIETY'S COLLECTIONS OF GLASS PAPER-weights was acquired in 1939 through the gift of Edwin Waitstill Orvis in memory of his wife, Carrie Emerton Orvis. It comprises eighty-two paperweights, many of them American. Several antique and modern paperweights were received by the society in 1952 as the gift of Mr. and Mrs. J. Insley Blair, who had also given to the society their collections of ceramics, chintzes, and pressed glass. By far the largest and most important of the society's paperweight collections is the bequest made in 1965 by Mrs. Jennie H. Sinclair, and known as the Francis MacDonald and Jennie H. Sinclair Collection. In the same year Mrs. Sinclair also gave to the society her collections of Toby jugs and early American glass.

The Francis MacDonald and Jennie H. Sinclair Collection of glass paperweights includes 439 paperweights, paperweight inkwells, paperweight vases, and sulphide wall plaques. This collection covers almost the entire range of European paperweight-making of the Classic period (1845–1855), and of American paperweight-making of the second half of the nineteenth and early twentieth centuries. Together, the society's collections possibly include more antique glass paperweights than any other collection in the world open to the public.

Jennie Hankinson Sinclair was born on February 16, 1869, and died at the age of ninety-six on March 7, 1965. Francis MacDonald Sinclair, who died in 1918, had been co-founder of the Sinclair & Valentine Co., makers of printing inks. Even before his death, Mrs. Sinclair had begun collecting glass paperweights, and paperweights became her favorites among the many things she collected. She was fond of day-long automobile excursions from their home in Wolfeboro, New Hampshire, on the shores of Lake Winnipesaukee, and she would stop at antique shops along the road looking for weights, but she was very particular about quality and did not always buy what she saw. In the mid-twenties Jennie Sinclair could be seen motoring about the countryside in her chauffeur-driven Locomobile, perhaps as far from home as Ogunquit, Maine, where there was a shop she frequented. Mrs. Sinclair also acquired weights at auction sales and on trips to Europe.

Over a long collecting life Mrs. Sinclair assembled an enormous collection of fine French and American paperweights. But she was as generous as she was acquisitive and gave many away. A friend remembers that she paid $2,500 for a lizard weight, which she later gave to him. Her final gift of paperweights was to the New-York Historical Society. The result of her enthusiasm, taste, and diligence, it is one of the finest collections of paperweights to be seen.

NOTE TO THE READER

FOR A DESCRIPTION OF ALL THE NEW-YORK HISTORICAL SOCIETY'S PAPERWEIGHTS see pages 139–205. Paperweights illustrated in the colorplates are approximately four-fifths actual size. Black-and-white illustrations have been reduced in many instances to present a uniform size. Actual diameters are always given.

   In this book the term "white glass" refers to opaque white. Uncolored glass is referred to as clear glass.

PART ONE

INTRODUCTION

THE AMBIENCE OF GLASS PAPERWEIGHTS

I

IN EUROPE IN THE 1840S THE STAGE WAS SET FOR THE APPEARANCE OF GLASS PAPER-weights. It was a time much like our own, of accelerating complexities and smoldering revolutions. With the technology of the Industrial Revolution and the accompanying rise in political liberalism, Europe had begun to pull itself out of the economic and agricultural structure of the Middle Ages and away from the autocratic monarchial systems that had compartmentalized life and stifled communication. A new mass culture was beginning to develop.

In England the *Art-Union Monthly Journal* (from 1843) and the *Journal of Design and Manufactures* (from 1849) evaluated the new culture by showing concern with the application of new manufacturing processes to the design of commercial products. Typically, the full name of the Society of Arts was the Society for the Encouragement of Arts, Manufactures and Commerce.

The horizons of the 1840s were broadened as much by the printed word as by the railroad: people traveled afield after reading in new books, magazines, and newspapers about life in their own and other lands. A growing middle class, better educated and better informed than heretofore, was making increasing use of the written word. By the early 1800s letter paper was being produced in a variety of sizes and weights. Penny postage began in 1840. For the middle and upper classes, supported as they were by an army of servants second only to farmers in the labor force, it was an indoor world of reading and correspondence. An American traveler in 1843, Henry Colman, notes that there was "what is always to be found in an English house, a writing-table, letter paper, notepaper, new pens, ink, sealing-wax, and wax taper, and a letterbox is kept in the house and notice given to the guests at what hour the post will leave." Colman's own letters, written while traveling, cover the years 1843 through 1849 and fill two volumes.[1]

To encourage the rapidly growing use of paper, stationery shops began to stock all manner of peripheral novelties. The steel pen, invented by Samuel Harrison of Birmingham in 1780, finally began to catch on in England in the 1830s. In the late 1840s stationers' shops sold desk and writing accessories such as millefiori and floral glass paperweights, ostensibly to hold down paper. Other millefiori items included inkwells, penholders—called shot cups for the buckshot that held pens—wafer trays to hold wax letter seals, even glass rulers; and in addition scent bottles, mantel ornaments, wig stands, wineglasses, and decanters. What would not fit on the desk or mantel was put on the whatnot, defined in the *Dictionary of Americanisms* (1848) as "In New York a piece of furniture usually placed in a parlor, consisting of several shelves, upon which are placed articles of vertu, porcelain, small bronzes, etc."[2] The "etc." included paperweights.

In 1848 there were said to be thirty thousand English living in Paris, and other English thought nothing of paying the city a casual visit. Thackeray in his *Paris Sketch Book* describes young fellows starting to grow moustaches for a weekend on the Continent, "as if their upper lips were smeared with snuff." Once they got across the seasick Channel, the journey from Boulogne to Paris took twenty-five hours by diligence, but they went and they brought back gifts—often such novelties as glass paperweights.

The timetable of the Industrial Revolution was slower in France and inventions were often successful in England or Germany first. The rotary steam printing press, which greatly speeded up printing, made its debut at the London *Times* in 1814 and only reached France a decade later. By 1837 it was used in England to print books, but not until 1844 in France. Following the Napoleonic wars France was held in political check by Europe, and the last years of the constitutional monarchy of Louis Philippe (1830–1848) were characterized by a policy of peace at any price. Under the bourgeois king the society of the salon flourished and baubles for the elite glittered in the boutiques of Paris. Bad harvests in France in 1845, paralleling the Irish potato famine, raised prices and lowered wages, but in Paris the gay life went on in spite of the depression. Indeed, two years later certain Sèvres porcelain vases were priced at $7,000 and dessert plates at $40 each; fabric for a ball gown cost $300 a yard and a dinner at the Hotel Meurice ran to $20. At the same time paperweights cost only a few

---

1 Henry Colman, *European Life and Manners; in Familiar Letters to Friends.* Boston: Charles C. Little and James Brown, and London: John Peterham, 1849.
2 John Russell Bartlett, *Dictionary of Americanisms.* New York: Bartlett and Welford, 1848.

francs and were readily available to the new bourgeoisie.

It was a loaded political situation that was to push France to the brink of the abyss. The first slaughter of the Revolution in February of 1848 missed Henry Colman by five minutes; sixty-two persons were killed or wounded on the spot where he had been standing. Yet two weeks later our American traveler was able to write:

> *I passed through the Passage de l'Opéra last evening, and saw the usual immense crowd rushing into the doors of the* Bal Masqué, *in all the fever and intoxication of gaiety and joy. . . . I went to the Théâtre des Variétés, where I found a crowded house, and the people enjoying, with their usual gay humor, the admirable acting of Lafont and that* diablesse *Déjazet, and all the jokes and buffoonery of the play, with the same zest as if, during the last fortnight, the streets instead of being sprinkled with blood had only been decorated with roses.*

In another letter of the same date he writes: "Excepting the shops which supply articles of food and clothing, the great proportion of the shops of Paris are trading in articles of mere luxury, in which they abound to an extraordinary degree." His reference would certainly have included the "fancy" shop in the rue de Richelieu of Jacquel, who in the mid-1840s billed himself as sole purveyor to the king and royal household, supplying crystal from Baccarat, Saint-Louis, and Clichy. It also would have included the famous Escalier de Cristal in the Palais-Royal, which supplied tripod tables, chairs, and huge vases—all made of glass with bronze decoration—to such of the nobility as the Duchesse de Berry and the Comte d'Artois. Like their English counterparts, French stationery shops sold all manner of fancy glass goods, including, of course, paperweights and paperweight inkstands. For as bibelots glass paperweights were in the mainstream of the decorative arts of the late 1840s.

II

The history of the decorative arts is a record of imitation, of revival and transformation. Roman glass vessels made for household use from about 100 B.C. in Alexandria to A.D. 100 in Rome included glass dishes and bowls whose fabric supported a millefiori design composed of thin slices of colored glass cane. The art of millefiori apparently was revived in Renaissance Venice, but few examples remain from that era, and certain of those millefiori vessels are now thought to date from succeeding centuries. A genuine large-scale millefiori revival did occur in Europe in the fourth and fifth decades of the nineteenth century, although one is hinted at as early as 1786 in the suggestion by a German of a way to re-create the ancient Roman millefiori glass. The Classic period of paperweight-making is approximately from 1845 to 1855.

The millefiori revival of the early Victorian period seems to have been one of spontaneous generation, for it sprang up simultaneously in Bohemia-Silesia, Venice, and France. But the imitative aspect of this revival was confined during the 1840s to the general process by which the millefiori canes were made—that is, by dipping pontil rods into pots of variously colored glass or by forming the canes in molds. Once the canes were made, pulled, cooled, and sliced, the imitative phase ended. Except as incidental objects, few millefiori household vessels were made until the Salviati and Venezia-Murano companies were formed in the mid-sixties in Venice. Instead, the canes were arranged decoratively within a solid dome of transparent glass that both magnified the designs and sealed them off from the touch. This invention was the millefiori glass paperweight, at once useful and mysterious.

The earliest date that appears in paperweights—1845—can be found in examples from Venice (made in Murano) and from the Saint-Louis factory in France. The Murano scrambled examples required no particular skill beyond that which the Venetians already possessed from centuries of glassmaking. The French paperweights of 1845 are far superior to the Venetian and must have required several years of experimentation. Thus, it is reasonable to project the first French paperweight back to 1842 or 1843.

<h1 style="text-align:center">III</h1>

It is often said that paperweights were not commercial products and that they were made after hours privately as amusements, tests of skill, or as gifts or remembrances. While this was sometimes true, there is ample evidence that at the major French, English, and American factories paperweights were indeed commercial products. The Baccarat archives include a colored style sheet showing some of its well-known flower and butterfly paperweight designs. Even the sizes of the paperweights for which these designs were intended are specified. In the late 1840s, in the correspondence of Launay, head of Launay, Hautin & Cie., the Paris distributor for both Baccarat and Saint-Louis, there are specific references to the styling and marketing of paperweights. Launay cautions Saint-Louis against the poorly made weights the factory has been sending him and adds, "This item of manufacture has no sales merit unless it is well done." He proposes improvements in the styling of bouquets and warns Saint-Louis that Clichy appears to have captured the paperweight market.

Today, the sales catalogues of major auction houses such as Christie's and Sotheby's of London, and Sotheby's American subsidiary, Sotheby Parke Bernet of New York, indicate that Clichy did indeed capture the market from Baccarat and Saint-Louis. Many more Clichy weights come up for auction. Clichy, with its gaily striped baskets, its rich overlays, and its garlands on brightly colored grounds, seems to have grasped the essence of the Victorian aesthetic. The fact that there are no dated Saint-Louis weights after 1848, and only a few specifically commemorative dates from Baccarat after 1849, may be significant. Perhaps Clichy, which never bothered to date its paperweight products, was left the victor and went on producing weights for several years, long enough to swell today's auction catalogues.

Clichy was the only one of the big three French factories with enough foresight to send its glass to the Great Exhibition of 1851 in London, Saint-Louis and Baccarat having, as a member of the Institute of France put it, "deserted in the face of England and Bohemia." While no Clichy paperweights were inventoried or mentioned at the London exhibition, an engraving appears in the *Illustrated Exhibitor*, published during the exhibition, showing what is unquestionably a faceted Clichy scent bottle with millefiori design in both base and stopper (Fig. 1). It bears so striking a resemblance to one from the New-York Historical Society's Sinclair Collection (1965.607.C) that the possibility arises that it, too, may have been exhibited at the first World's Fair. We have the word of Horace Greeley that Clichy paperweights

FIG. I

were present "in all their variety" at the exhibition in New York's Crystal Palace in 1853.

A similar though quantitatively smaller and stylistically more limited commercial production than that of France is associated with English and American factories. In England, George Bacchus & Sons included paperweights in its exhibit in 1848 and 1849 in Birmingham. Both years the weights were written up in the *Art-Journal,* which also noted paperweights from the Islington Glass Works. Numerous Whitefriars weights and inkwells bear the 1848 date. In America, production continued at least through the 1870s: two flower weights are shown in a stereopticon slide of the Boston & Sandwich Glass Company exhibit of 1878 in Mechanics Hall, Boston, while from the rival New England Glass Company the previous year we have an interoffice memo saying that "for Tom's paper-weight goods I think I shall get between six and seven dollars, according to Mr. Brown's estimate."

As commercial products, paperweights represented the best that could be turned out in quantity at low cost. Considered in this light, the high quality of most French and many American paperweights is almost beyond belief. It indicates an inventive enthusiasm and a technical know-how combined in a way that would not be possible today—that, in fact, was not possible at any other time in history.

IV

But if paperweights are to be judged as commercial products, they must also be considered in the context of early Victorian decorative arts. Looking forward from the Empire and Restoration periods in France and the roughly corresponding Regency and early Victorian periods in England, the decorative trend in whatever medium—silver, textiles, furniture, or ceramics—was toward increased elaboration of all available surfaces with unrelated patterns. This trend saw experimentation with new manufacturing techniques put to the supposed service of a growing middle class, but it was also the handmaiden of a new and fastidious conservatism in both countries. For the eclectic romanticism of the early Victorian period ran counter to the possibilities opened up by the new techniques. After 1851, the conspicuous spending of the Second Empire in France and the smug prosperity of England were to provide even more reassuring symbols of the good life. By 1851 the apogee of hideousness in design had not yet been reached.

In glass, as in other areas, the trend was toward the same fussy complexity. The spare styles of the 1830s, the remains of the Georgian inheritance, receded before the cutter's tool and the painter's brush, and the form and function of vessels disappeared behind a camouflage of busy surfaces and extraneous ornament. The award of jury prizes at exhibitions in both countries acted as a spur to excellence, though the jurors themselves were frequently overcome by the florid *Zeitgeist.* From 1800 on, exhibitions, each one larger and more impressive than the last, replaced the medieval fairs that had served for so long as migrant bazaars and trading posts. The exhibitions of the 1840s were dress rehearsals for Prince Albert's first World's Fair. Here at last the wares of the world were on view, and each and every country could be judged on the quantity and quality of what it produced. Like designers in other mediums, glass stylists borrowed from everywhere: from Etruscan vases, from Bohemia, from chancels, chalices, and armored helmets, from Venice and Turkey, and from each other. They seemed to want to prove that glass could imitate any other material. As a writer in the *Art-Journal*'s illustrated catalogue of the Crystal Palace Exhibition put it, in referring to the Brooklyn Flint Glass Works, "There is enough novelty of form in these works to assure us that our transatlantic brethren are fully aware of the mercantile value of Art."

But paperweight makers succumbed to none of these excesses. Because of the enormous manipulative difficulties of the glass medium, which necessitated a symbolic abstraction of the various paperweight designs, whether cane or lampwork, paperweights were saved from the literalism that afflicted Victorian painting, sculpture, and the decorative arts. The abstracted design was further enhanced by the dome of clear glass that sealed it off from prying investigation while preserving the ambivalence of its identity. Everything inside a glass paperweight is either smaller or larger than it appears under the magnifying or concave-faceted dome, and this compounds its mystery.

Furthermore, while the millefiori glass paperweight was unquestionably a Victorian invention, the millefiori part of it derived both its inspiration and its technique from Alexandria and Rome. The old millefiori technique, to be sure, is adapted to a new use, and the appearance of the brilliant new canes is transformed under the spotlight of the glass dome, but a sense of the ancient millefiori ritual remains. In no other decorative usage of the Victorian period was there this feeling of the dependence between ancestor and descendant, between borrowed and borrower. In most Victorian objects the borrowed design is only skin deep and we have no trouble recognizing the object as Victorian. The applied arts *are* applied. In glass paperweights the arrangements and color schemes are Victorian, but they float in a dome of glass and they do not overpower the medium. Looking into a fine paperweight, we can sense that glassmaking is alchemy and that glass paperweights are the alchemist's dream.

PAPERWEIGHT-MAKING

Paperweight-making was and is one of the best kept secrets of glassmaking, a traditionally secretive profession. It is likely that more than one person was involved in the complicated process, and that, for certain operations, a whole team of glassworkers may have assisted the gaffer. There were three basic ways to make a paperweight design: with millefiori canes, by lampwork, and by crimping. Numerous examples of all three processes may be seen in the Sinclair Collection.

MILLEFIORI

In the millefiori process a supply of millefiori glass canes was essential for a varied and interesting design. The basic tool for making a cane was the long iron pontil rod, to the end of which the necessary gather of nearly molten glass was attached. This bloblike gather of glass, usually white* or colored rather than clear, was rolled on a flat surface called a marver to give it a lengthened cylindrical form. It thus became the core, or center, of the cane and, if the cane design called for it to be star-shaped, it could be reheated at the furnace and

---

*In this book "white" always refers to opaque white as opposed to clear glass.

FIG. 2

plunged into a star-shaped iron mold, whose shape it retained on withdrawal. It could then be taken to the furnace again and given a coating of glass of a contrasting color, or perhaps two successive coatings of different colors, and the process repeated with a variety of molds until a compound design of colored glass was achieved. This was a cane: a solid cylinder perhaps two inches thick and six inches long, and still attached to the end of the pontil rod.

At this point the glass was still very hot, and a worker assisting the gaffer attached another pontil rod with a small gather of hot glass to the free end of the large cane. While the cane was still ductile the two men, facing each other, with the cane held horizontally between the two horizontal pontil rods, moved backward away from one another, stretching out the cane like taffy candy until it was perhaps fifty feet long and no thicker than a lead pencil. As shown in this illustration taken from Apsley Pellatt's Falcon Glass Works (Fig. 2), a third man is cooling the lengthening cane, by fanning it with his hat as it is laid on the track that keeps it off the floor. After the cane had cooled it could be cut into many hundreds of thin slices, each slice a cross section showing the identical design, for, of course, the design ran all the way through the cane from end to end.

But this represented only one design, and millefiori paperweights required canes of many different designs. Thus, a sufficient supply of canes might take months to make. Once made, however, a single cane could supply cane slices for parts of many paperweight designs, a fact demonstrated when one recognizes slices from the same cane—with its individual telltale construction—in a variety of paperweights.

Supplies of cane slices were very likely kept, much as type faces are, in compartmented trays, where they could be selected by the paperweight designer and placed in the desired pattern in the saucerlike bed or flat circle that would contain the paperweight design. It did not matter too much if the slices were not all exactly of the same thickness, because the concave bed that aligned the bottoms of the canes became the convex top of the design.

The next step undoubtedly involved the gaffer who headed the team of glassworkers.

Holding a pontil (or punty) rod vertically over the design—a rod on the lower end of which was a gather of viscous clear glass—the gaffer carefully let the rod descend onto the design to embed it in the malleable glass. He then took the rod with its design-bearing gather to the gaffer's chair, where with one hand he rolled the rod forward and backward on the gently sloping arms of the chair, while with the other hand he shaped the gather with an applewood block dipped in a bucket of water to prevent it from charring against the extremely hot glass. Several trips to the furnace and much shaping were required to cover the design with the solid dome of clear glass that so mysteriously transforms it. In about a half hour the paper-weight had assumed its final shape and size, and the gaffer carried the pontil rod once again to the furnace, where the heat fire-polished the domed surface of the weight, making it smooth and even in contour. Finally, the gaffer took the weight to a table, where he cracked it off the pontil rod with a sharp, deft blow from a file or other handy instrument. That ended the gaffer's role in the production.

The weight was then put in an annealing oven: in big glassworks a long heated tunnel in which the heat decreased as glassware was pushed slowly toward the far end on metal trays. On removal from the annealing oven a new department of the factory took over such finishing steps as grinding off the pontil mark and occasionally cutting facets to enhance the design. If the clear glass surface of the weight had been overlaid with coatings of one or more colors, punties or windows had to be cut through the overlay to show the interior design, and this was done with a series of lathe-turned wheels, beginning with a cast-iron wheel fed with a mud slurry mixed with sand, for roughing out the punty. Next a natural sandstone wheel smoothed the cut, leaving a lightly frosted surface. A wooden wheel polished the cut and a high shine was sometimes imparted to the glass by a felt buff containing a bit of tin oxide. A few paperweights were engraved or painted with floral designs.

LAMPWORK

The lampwork process was used to make glass paperweight designs of fruits, flowers, butterflies, birds, and animals. A lamp or torch softened the glass rods until they could be shaped and tooled, trailed onto and fused to one another to form the desired object. An ingenious flexible interchange of glass parts took place in lampworking, and in the old paperweights of the Classic period the same veined shape might be used to represent both a leaf and a flower petal. Different flowers were suggested by a rearrangement of the same parts; the glass medium dictated the vocabulary.

After the lampwork object was assembled, it was picked up, as was the millefiori design, by a hot glass blob on the end of the pontil, except that special care had to be taken not to fracture the thin glass assembly. Lampwork paperweights were made in the same years as millefiori paperweights and often included millefiori canes in the designs. In France a second surge of paperweight-making took place about the time of the Exposition Universelle de 1878, and it is thought that certain weights showing lampwork flowers modeled in high relief were made at this time, possibly by the Pantin factory of Monot et Stumpf.

CRIMPING

The crimping process was different from either millefiori or lampwork. It involved the use of a metal crimp in the form of a rose, tulip, or water lily, or shaped like an umbrella. After the original blob of clear glass was shaped, a wad or blob of colored glass was attached to it, probably by another worker with a pontil rod, and the crimp was then used to force the colored glass wad into the clear glass, imparting to it in the process the flower form of the crimp. American paperweights were made with a crimp in the early years of this century, notably by four glassworkers at the Whitall Tatum factory in Millville, New Jersey, and somewhat later by Emil Larsen in nearby Vineland.

COLLECTING PAPERWEIGHTS

The story of paperweight collecting begins with royalty and the nobility. The Second Empire (1852–1870) was a time of great public works. Under Napoleon III Baron Hauss-mann rebuilt Paris. The glass that formerly had gone into delicate latticinio perfume bottles and paperweights was now used for the large mirrors and ponderous chandeliers of the great new mansions and public buildings lining the boulevards. No longer available as gifts or souvenirs to anyone with a few francs in his pocket, paperweights began to be collected seriously by the emperor's own wife, the empress Eugénie. The princess Murat and the duke of Cardoza were collectors, and so was the empress Carlotta, the unfortunate wife of Emperor Maximilian of Mexico. Perhaps as a result of her interest antique French paperweights are still collected in Mexico. The royal collections of England include fine French paperweights from the collection of Queen Mary, perhaps inherited from Queen Victoria.

As time went on others began collecting. Oscar Wilde was one, and the weights he once owned have filtered into today's private and public collections. Colette, too, collected them, and some of her weights she later gave to an admiring Truman Capote. Through the first four decades of this century paperweight collecting went on unaided by anything other than the instinct and enthusiasm of the collector. Then, in 1939, the first book on the subject appeared, Francis Edgar Smith's *American Glass Paperweights,* and the next year Evangeline H. Berg-strom's pioneering and important *Old Glass Paperweights.* Though printed privately in small editions, their effect, particularly that of Mrs. Bergstrom's book, was to stimulate the collecting of paperweights. During the 1940s many new collectors entered the lists and old collections changed hands. One of the largest collections assembled during those years and since disbursed was that of S. Weldon O'Brien which, according to the late collector, numbered at its zenith some fifteen hundred weights. But it was not until after World War II that paperweights began to appear regularly at auction sales in London and New York. Beginning with the Applewhaite-Abbott sales of 1952 and 1953, and the sale of ex-King Farouk's paperweights in 1954, paperweight collecting became prestigious.

Paperweights are the crown jewels of collecting and this book is intended not only as a catalogue of the paperweights in the New-York Historical Society's paperweight collections but also to aid the novice in becoming familiar with the examples from the collections illustrated here. After a few tours of inspection the viewer should be able to distinguish in a general way between paperweights of the Classic period and the countless modern weights to be found in gift shops and department stores everywhere. Familiarity with fine old paperweights will enable the beginning collector to identify quality workmanship.

For the seasoned and careful observer, the Sinclair Collection can answer questions by

FIG. 3

example, showing a torsade in yellow in a Saint-Louis upright bouquet, a fourth type of Baccarat pansy, the unusual sorts of weights made by Bacchus, and many other variations both common and rare.

For the new as well as for the seasoned collector there are a few cautionary thoughts not to be found in most of the books and articles on paperweights:

1. A reputable paperweight dealer will not knowingly misrepresent the provenance of a paperweight. But dealers do not like to handle a weight to which they cannot put a name, and they are prone to the uniqueness syndrome. They are likely to believe that any type of weight unknown to them is, ipso facto, unique. Uniqueness, of course, has its own special property of being one and one only, and the antidote to the notion of uniqueness is familiarity with the range of what was made.

2. Rarity in a paperweight is sometimes a mask for mediocrity. Just as some of the rarest paperweights are very beautiful, others are not; beauty lies in the look of the weight itself, not in its rarity. A rare weight means that not many examples were made. The reason for this may have been that the weight was exceedingly difficult to make and production was therefore limited, perhaps to the one person who could make that weight. More often, however, rarity is an indication that the design was not considered successful or salable. Rare paperweights are often nothing but discontinued models. Nevertheless, an attractive rare weight is something for which most collectors search.

3. Some collectors rely on the long-wave ultraviolet lamp, familiarly known as the "black light," to help them decide the provenance of a paperweight. While the UV lamp is known to be very useful in the detection of such things as the retouching of paintings and repairs made on porcelains and furniture, it is not designed to indicate anything more about glass than the presence of certain fluorescent elements in the chemical composition. The assignment of differently colored fluorescences to various factories is unreliable in terms of glass-making in the 1840s, when glass content varied from batch to batch. The "black light" has become the lazy collector's substitute for learning the characteristics of paperweights from different factories.

4. In deciding whether a weight of a certain type—say, a brightly colored clematis or dahlia on a latticinio ground—is French or American, observation of its profile in comparison with the nearest available French paperweight is likely to be useful. Observe both weights from the side at eye level if possible, or if not, by tilting them to the same degree. If the domed silhouette of the weight in question is low and slightly flatter on top in comparison to the French example, and if the base is only slightly concave, the weight is probably an American one from Sandwich. But if the profile is at least as tall, relative to diameter, as the French profile, and if the base is deeply hollowed out, with a wavy or double rim, then the weight is probably from the New England Glass Company.

5. Profile condition is very important in determining the long-term value of a paper-weight. Every year, due to shipping, dropping, or general wear and tear, damaged paper-weights are sent to be reground and the bruises or other blemishes removed; and occasionally regrinding is necessary to save a paperweight from oblivion. But collectors, disturbed by scratched surfaces, and dealers, anxious to improve the appearance of their stock, regularly send their weights out for regrinding. As a result each year fewer and fewer paperweights look as they did when they were made; fewer, that is, wear their original profile. Regrinding alters this highly important feature in the identification and the character of a paperweight. When paperweights were made they were shaped for optimum viewing and fire-polished to a smooth, evenly curved finish. Make no mistake about it, no matter how skillfully a weight may be reground, regrinding can never duplicate the original curve; it can only diminish the weight.

For the prospective buyer there are two easy ways to detect regrinding. One is to rotate the weight with one hand against the cupped fingertips of the other, to sense the surface irregularities regrinding always leaves. If the fingertips are too moist, a facial tissue held between weight and fingertips will permit the glass to slide more smoothly. If you should happen to lack fingertip sensitivity, simply turn the paperweight slowly and evenly from side to side against a light source and observe the path the light takes over the surface. If it wobbles, the weight has been reground. In a weight that has not been reground the light seldom wobbles, staggers, or jumps. Do not be misled by the term "repolished." Except in the case of minor scratches, "repolished" is a euphemism for "reground." Where your paperweight has moons, that means deep bruises, and as much as three-sixteenths or a quarter of an inch of surface may have to be ground away; afterward it will not be the same paperweight. Paperweights in good untouched condition are becoming increasingly hard to find, and they are consequently more valuable.

6. Regrinding, unfortunately, has been used by ignorant or thoughtless dealers and collectors to remake paperweights into supposedly more important and valuable examples. Fine weights that have been damaged, or unimportant and poorly made unfaceted weights, are now being cut with facets to hide or disguise damage or internal defects in the design or to break up the appearance of large bubbles. Usually this faceting is inconsistent with the faceting style of the maker, and it helps to confuse paperweight provenance. Downright vandalism has been practiced on old weights, such as the removal of color grounds and the recutting of overlay work to make a weight appear fancier. Stay clear of such paperweights no matter how rare they are said to be. New faceting, incidentally, is easy to detect, because the edges of the cuts are usually rounded and gentle to the touch, and there are no bruises or chips; whereas the edges of original faceting are usually precise and sharp, and there are likely to be a few wear-and-tear nicks.

7. Do not buy a paperweight that does not please you; do not buy one you do not like.

8. A balanced collection with good examples of various types from different factories is always a pleasing sight. However, some collectors have predilections for certain kinds of weights and are partial to one factory over another. And occasional collectors are always on the lookout for offbeat paperweights that contain unusual variations on familiar themes. Any approach to collecting is good so long as the examples chosen are well made and attractive.

Yet, perhaps too great emphasis is placed upon perfection. We tend to forget that paperweights were made to sell for only a few francs, pounds, or dollars, and that as hand-made objects they were subject not only to the habits and capabilities of the artists who made them but also to wide variations in the quality and content of the glass. Paperweight-making was an art, not a science.

Since paperweights have become status symbols for collectors, cost has often, alas, dictated desirability. While some weights are vigorously contested at auction, others go begging. In general, it is better to own an inexpensive paperweight with a design that is beautifully executed than an ambitious and very expensive example with flaws.

PART TWO

THE COLORPLATES

THE RANGE OF NINETEENTH-CENTURY PAPERWEIGHT-MAKING SHOWN IN THESE COL-
orplates, made up primarily of examples taken from the Sinclair Collection, provides a vivid
picture of variations within set forms, of cross-fertilizing influences, and of freedom yet
interdependence among factories in creating and satisfying the public fancy.

In a departure from the usual procedure in paperweight literature, the paperweights
illustrated in color have been grouped according to type regardless of factory, so that the eye
may take in variations on a single theme and learn the look of the many forms. Plates 1
through 92 illustrate the Continental and English weights in the New-York Historical Society's collections. American paperweights, Plates 93 through 119, while generally made by
European émigrés strongly influenced by European styles, are, it is felt, more instructively
presented as a separate group. Hence they follow the European weights in illustration as they
did in time. Plate 120, the final plate, shows three modern Scottish paperweights.

SCRAMBLED WEIGHTS

The term "scrambled,"—like its synonyms: pell-mell, macédoine—suggests the random appearance of these weights. A gather of glass on the end of a pontil rod is used to pick up bits of millefiori, filigree, and other colored glass spread on the marver or within the bed ring. The weight is then completed in the same manner as other millefiori weights described in the introduction.

PLATE I

Scrambled weights form the bases of a pair of Saint-Louis wafer dishes at the top of the plate, with blue ruffle-rimmed bowls, which sound the Angelus when tapped, because of the high lead content. Filigree and twisted color rods abound in Saint-Louis scrambleds, a surprising number of which form the bases of vessels. The shot cups in the center are further instances. Their lovely inverted bell-shaped cups enclose a vertical spiral arrangement of five-stranded latticinio separated by blue rods. The outer surface of the cups is spirally trailed in a mold, with the mold marks visible. In the Clichy scrambled weight, bottom right, the fragments of colored glass are tightly crammed, while in the Baccarat one, bottom left, the filigree twist rods are set at right angles in typical Baccarat style. There is a simple way to distinguish between makers: when viewed horizontally Baccarat filigree twists slant to the left, whereas Saint-Louis and Clichy twists slant to the right.

CLOSE MILLEFIORI

The term "millefiori" describes the effect of many canes seen in proximity. "Close" millefiori refers to the close vertical packing together of the canes, like people in a dense crowd. The patchwork quilt of one hundred or one hundred and fifty canes in a close millefiori paperweight offers a sampling of many or most of the canes made by a factory, and treats the eye to almost endless variety. It is difficult to make an accurate count of the number of canes in a close millefiori weight three inches in diameter; and equally difficult to tabulate or even analyze the variety and number of component rods among the canes.

The next two plates afford an opportunity to observe different factory approaches to similar objects and designs. In Baccarat close millefiori weights, the canes are packed in a three-dimensional cushion shape, with the outer canes drawn in toward the center of the base and only the canes at the very top of the cushion set in vertically. In spite of the close packing, spaces appear between the canes near the top of the cushion due to the slightly differing angles at which the canes are set. The light that might otherwise penetrate these clear glass spaces has been cleverly eliminated by stuffing the inside of the cushion with white filigree. The method by which this was accomplished is one of the many secrets of paperweight-making. In close millefiori weights from the Clichy factory the canes are close-packed verti-

cally in a flattened dome, with the bottoms of the canes broken off irregularly a short distance below their smoothly ground tops, but these irregularities are then hidden behind a sheath of staves whose tops are level with the design and follow the curve of the weight to the base. Opacity in the motif is achieved by the close vertical proximity of the canes and by the sheath of staves that cuts out the light below the canes. The stave sheath or basket was an important and effective design element at Clichy.

PLATE 2

The center piece of this group is a Baccarat wafer dish signed and dated, with its figure canes, its spirally twisted rim, and its bowl beautifully engraved with rosebushes—a triumph of Victorian glassmaking.

PLATE 3

Four of the five Clichy weights pictured in Plates 2 and 3, an extraordinarily high percentage, are signed with the initial "C" in one cane. In addition to the signature, the one at the top left contains uncommon blue, green, and yellow Clichy roses. The center weight has been tilted to show its purple and white stave basket.

SPACED MILLEFIORI

Spaced millefiori refers to designs in which the canes are spaced apart, either at set distances or at random. In Plates 4 and 5, examples in assorted sizes from the three major French factories show pronounced differences.

PLATE 4

In Baccarat spaced millefiori arrangements the outer canes are placed alternately high and low. Sometimes, as in the weight at the top dated "B. 1847," the arrangement is given extra life by the inclusion of brightly colored rods and twists in the lace ground. The early Clichy example at right, with less subtlety in cane coloring and cruder rose petals than were achieved later, nevertheless shows the beginnings of the checker form, with its filigree canes set at right angles about the millefiori canes and its parallel placement of long filigree canes beneath the ground. The large size of this weight and its unscratched flat base suggest it may have been used as a newel-post finial. The arrowhead rods of the weight at left, unlike those from Baccarat, resemble an anchor. The great modern paperweight maker Charles Kaziun has indicated that making this kind of rod was, and is, no easy matter. The chartreuse coloring of these rods is typical of Saint-Louis.

PLATE 5

In the center weight the chartreuse canes are set flush with a blue and white hassock-shaped jasper ground, another Saint-Louis specialty. The uncommon 1849 date appears in the weight above.

CONCENTRIC MILLEFIORI

Plates 6 through 11 show a variety of concentrics from all three French factories. Together with and perhaps even more than close millefiori, the concentrics epitomize mid-nineteenth-century paperweight-making. The results are often exciting and generally of good quality; it seems to have been the natural design to fit the circular form of the paperweight. Looking at a good concentric, one feels this was what paperweights were meant to be. Concentrics are either close—that is, having the rows or rings closely set—or open, with the rings separated by clear glass or a color ground.

PLATE 6

This is a superb large Clichy close concentric with a ring of pink roses among other predominately green and white canes, resting in a basket of white and unusual translucent blue staves. It has the important presence and tightly woven texture of a fine oriental rug. The carrying power of its simple pattern of alternating rings of like and alternating canes places it with the finer objects in the decorative arts.

PLATE 7

The tulip-cut overlay shot cup in the center, with paperweight base, is one of two Baccarat concentrics in the society's collections, and shows once again the practical yet fanciful use of paperweights as bases for desk and ornamental articles. The blue flashing on the petal edges of the cup shows Bohemian influence.

PLATE 8

Typical concentrics are the Baccarat miniature at the top, two faceted Clichy examples, left and right, and the delicate Clichy at top right on lace ground. The signed but not dated Saint-Louis weight at the bottom is less frequently encountered. Like many but by no means all Saint-Louis concentrics, the alignment of the rows is somewhat wobbly. Perhaps such examples were made by one man, or perhaps it was a case of miscalculation and the signature canes were not allowed for—who knows? In any event, the signature together with the central cane of dancing figures and the four dog silhouettes in the next-to-outer ring make this a desirable paperweight. It also happens to contain one of those charming secrets we sometimes stumble on: the small pink whorl canes immediately outside the central figure cane each have center rods showing the same dog silhouettes, pulled out so fine that they can only be seen with a magnifying glass. One of the canes in this row has slipped into the next row during assembly.

PLATE 9

Two Clichy spaced concentrics, the larger with a translucent cranberry ground, the miniature showing lavender-sheathed roses on an opaque turkey-red ground. The contrast there is interesting not·only in size but in the difference between the two reds, one seen in the transmitted light of the translucent ground, the other in the reflected light of the opaque ground. In most opaque-ground weights the color is applied to both the upper and lower surfaces of the opaque white ground. But the grounds are always fully encased in glass. In cases where the color ground reaches the outer surface of the weight, showing its color or its white lining—which presence may often be felt with the fingernail—this means that the weight has been reduced in size by regrinding, usually to remove bruises or other external defects. However, in Clichy weights such as the larger one pictured, there is frequently a thin indentation circling the weight just below the level of the ground, which has something to do with how the weight was made and does not indicate regrinding.

PLATE 10

The blue violet color ground at bottom right is rare. Interestingly, the most brilliant color grounds are often associated with a reduced palette of cane coloring, which shows the concern with color balance.

PLATE II

The Clichy scarlet or pigeon-blood ground, bottom, and the apple green ground, top, are uncommon and much desired. In addition, the latter is signed with a "C." Clichy color grounds are among the most colorful paperweights of the Classic period.

PANELED MILLEFIORI

Of the variously patterned millefiori weights the paneled design was used least, perhaps because it was easier to think circular and panels segment circularity.

PLATE 12

These paneled weights show the Clichy factory's rather elaborate attempts to achieve variety. The hexagonal design, top right, on deep ultramarine blue over white ground is signed "C" in the center cane—signatures rarely occur in the center. The predominance of canes in only two colors (pink and white) place this weight close to the carpet-ground category. In the uncommon Clichy example, top left, and the rare one, bottom left, the design is more obvious and the canes are sunk into the grounds, their tops level. The execution of the spoked design of the latter is particularly fine. The center Saint-Louis weight is something quite different. Here the alternating panels of rather crude blue and white and red and white jasper are

separated by rather crude white spokes. The delicate cane in each panel is lost against such a background. The central figure cane here has never been satisfactorily described. Looked at in one direction it seems to be a silhouette of Punch, Punchinello, or Guignol; in another it looks like an anteater or aardvark. A further interesting feature of this weight is that the jasper ground is double ply, the bottom layer composed of a mixture of all three jasper colors rather than alternations of two colors. Not visible from the top is a finely woven red and white filigree torsade that, taken with the diverse elements mentioned, is indicative of experimental work at the Saint-Louis factory, perhaps as early as 1845.

PLATE 13

In this Saint-Louis weight we see four panels of close millefiori divided by a cross of canes bordered in pistachio green (a favorite Saint-Louis color) and five-threaded filigree corkscrews. One cane shows a dog silhouette. These rare weights vary in quality, but this example is superb.

GARLANDS

The term "garland" covers all the sorts of looped, interwoven, wavy trefoil and qua- trefoil, and circular arrangements of millefiori canes; every imaginable garden border in clear glass or over color grounds. Though Baccarat and Saint-Louis made a fair try at garland weights, by far the greater number come from Clichy; garlands are Clichy trademarks.

PLATE 14

Like a ballet on a lawn, the red and white garland of this Clichy magnum is set in a carpet ground of green grass (moss) canes whose center is a red-centered white rod.

PLATE 15

This Clichy group includes a five-pointed star with a rose in the center, bottom, seen here on a lace ground, and a garland, left, of two intertwined pink and green quatrefoils on lace, with long parallel filigree strands beneath to give body to the ground. Another hallmark of Clichy styling in this example is the cutting of vertical flutes between the punties. In addition to Clichy roses, the weight of the top has its garlands in the shape of a C. The faceting of the weight, however, is what we would expect from Saint-Louis. The scent bottle reiterates the C-shaped garlands of the weight at the top and the cutting of the one to the left, but here the oval punties are raised medallions in the Bohemian-derived French style of the 1840s. In contrast to the garland on lace in the base of the bottle, the stopper has a concentric arrangement, but both base and stopper center the Clichy rose. This scent bottle is virtually identical in shape to the one appearing in *The Illustrated Exhibitor,* published in conjunction with the Great Exhibition of 1851 in London (see Fig. 1, p. 6). It has been mislabeled "Enamelled Water-Jug."

PLATE 16

At top right the rich Clichy cerulean ground supports six touching circles of canes. In Baccarat garlands the circles do not touch. Amethyst, red, and apple green are the least common ground colors. Saint-Louis garlands are rare. The deep salmon pink ground, top left, and the citron yellow ground, center right, are extremely rare. The perfection of these two weights is extraordinary. The flat faceting of the salmon pink example is unusual and probably not original; it may have been an attempt to distract attention from some small inclusions of unfused silica. The two marbrie weights, center left and bottom right, may have been made as a pair.

CARPET GROUNDS

Well done carpet grounds are among the loveliest weights. The term is suggested by the carpetlike effect of closely compacted canes or rods of the same design and color.

PLATE 17

In addition to the carpet of canes, the green Baccarat example at bottom is dated "B. 1848," the only carpet ground date known at Baccarat. The figure canes were apparently forced into the ground, in distinct contrast to the Saint-Louis carpets, center and top, where the ground canes are packed in evenly about the accent canes. As here, the Saint-Louis carpets are often slightly smaller in diameter than the Baccarat carpets. The lower canes of the Saint-Louis carpets draw together at the base, while at Baccarat there is often a gap of clear glass revealing the interior filigree stuffing.

PLATE 18

This Saint-Louis weight has an extremely rare carpet ground in coral pink, white, and blue, possibly suggestive of the tricolor which made one of its periodic appearances during the Revolution of 1848. In keeping with the simple coloring the canes too are plain, the blue and coral being bundles of unadorned rods and the white, star rods.

MUSHROOMS

The term "mushroom" describes the appearance of the motif seen in profile. Mushrooms are the most numerous of the upright forms and, like the upright bouquets, are, except for Clichy, encircled by a torsade. The mushrooms in Plates 19 through 24 cover virtually the total range of French production from all three factories.

PLATE 19

Close millefiori mushrooms from Baccarat and Clichy in a variety of cuttings. Like all Clichy mushrooms, the ones at bottom center and far left are faceted and lack the torsade at the base. The mushroom cap or tuft is flatter-domed than at Baccarat, and the stem of the mushroom is sheathed in staves. Included are two Clichy doorknobs in stave baskets, top center and bottom right. The Clichy mushrooms here all contain a variety of roses. It will be noted that Baccarat torsades spiral to the left. The center weight from Baccarat is faceted but without a top window, usually a Saint-Louis custom on some dahlia weights.

PLATE 20

These mushrooms are all concentrics. Except for a few early examples from 1845, the concentric arrangement is common to Saint-Louis. It is less common to Baccarat. The faceted Saint-Louis weight at top right lacks the torsade but is exquisitely formed and colored. Expert faceting exactly centers the mushroom cap and repeats the image. Saint-Louis mushroom bases are frequently star cut, Baccarat nearly always.

PLATE 21

Everything about the Baccarat weight at bottom left is unusual: its flat-cut top and flat side panels between the punties, its white stave sheath, and particularly its eleven Clichy-like roses, which must hold the record for a Baccarat weight. The stem of the colorful mushroom illustrated at center is sheathed in amethyst canes not visible from the top. Its torsade is topped by a continuous circular bubble (often mistakenly called a mercury bubble) that is almost certainly an unintended result of assembly problems. The beautifully fashioned Clichys at top left and right and bottom right appear respectively with stave sheaths in green and white, all-white, and pink and white; and the last has a variety of Clichy roses, including a ring of infrequently seen green roses. The base of the weight at top right is petal cut; the other bases are star cut.

PLATE 22

The amber-flashed base of the Saint-Louis weight at the top and the coral pink spiral torsade of the bottom one are in pleasant contrast and illustrate the imaginative variety to be encountered within a single form. The workmanship of the latter is superb.

PLATE 23

The mushroom form was also popular inside the double overlay. The bases of the three turquoise blue Clichy double overlays are typically crosshatched, while the cobalt blue Baccarat shows the Baccarat basal star. Again the Clichy examples are sheathed in staves, the stave tops, bottom left, being slightly hooked. And again it should be mentioned that the staves cover up and extend below the short canes of the tuft, forming the stem of the mushroom. Perhaps it was felt that the canes forming the Baccarat and Saint-Louis mushroom stems presented an irregular appearance, as indeed they generally do. Clichy top facets are usually flat, and side windows (usually five in number) flat or very slightly concave. At all factories when a mushroom was double overlaid the torsade was considered unnecessary.

PLATE 24

A lovely mushroom group, the top weight a white single overlay, rare in Clichy, in pink and white stave sheath. The tight even packing of the canes and the skillful control of color placements make this weight a fully realized example of the paperweight maker's art. The Saint-Louis weight in the center has a coral spiral torsade subtly placed beneath the tuft so as to border the design, while the one at the bottom is a small mushroom and needs no torsade. Not many small mushrooms were made.

PLATE 25

Two magnum-size mushrooms with blue and white spiral torsades from George Bacchus & Sons of Birmingham, England, the one at top left virtually a carpet ground of ruffled canes. Though perhaps only two dozen mushrooms were made, it is interesting to see that the manufacturers were able to eliminate the circular air bubble that plagues the French mushroom torsades. The other Bacchus weight at right is an extremely rare pink and white encased overlay basket with handle that must have been very difficult to produce. The interior tuft of flowers in the basket is made like the Baccarat mushroom and pulled out so finely below that the whole design appears reduced to less than one-half inch at the center of the base. Aside from Bacchus, only Saint-Louis is known to have made encased overlays.

PEDESTALS

Pedestal weights are paperweights having a prominent basal section, either in the form of a flange, or with a flange surmounted by a drum, perhaps in turn topped by another flange or ring.

PLATE 26

The Clichy pedestals here are all of the drum-on-flange type, the drum sheathed in vertical staves. The beautiful weight at bottom left, with its little button of roses in pink and white stave basket, and the delicate palette of the one at top left are Clichy at its best. The only nonconcentric in the group is the cross-paneled center one, whose pedestal is a latticinio basket ringed with a filigree twist.

PLATE 27

A Saint-Louis concentric filigree on pedestal, signed and dated, the date inserted in reverse, undoubtedly in error. In making millefiori paperweights the craftsman has usually to begin with the motif upside down and therefore backward. This superb weight suggests a rose window.

PLATE 28

This is a view of the bottom of the pedestal weight seen in the center of Plate 26, showing the fine latticinio and filigree twist. Note the pattern of the canes drawn into the center of the base.

SWIRLS

The swirl, a Clichy specialty, is one of the simplest and most effective paperweight designs, deriving its name from the spiral placement of the colored rods. It is interesting to note that stripes appeared in English fabrics after 1824 and were increasingly popular in the thirties and forties.

PLATE 29

Unlike the Clichy swirls with which it is classed, the Clichy spoke weight in the center shows straight rods like the spokes of a wheel. Perhaps it was the model for the Bohemian weight to the right of it, a rare weight made during the same years, just as the Clichy swirls on this and the next plate were models for the Bohemian swirl at bottom left. But Clichy made do with a single center cane.

PLATE 30

Three-color swirls like the Clichy weights at center and top are uncommon and much sought after. The pink and white swirl at bottom right is desirable too, for it centers a green and white Clichy rose.

CROWNS

The crown form refers to a vertically ribbed arrangement within the walls of a blown and flattened sphere. The vertical elements of the design are twisted ribbons and filigree, usually alternating, whose axis is a single cane that conceals the joining members. In France they were made only at the Saint-Louis factory, but they were also made in America (see Plate 95).

PLATE 31

The great rarity of Plate 31 is the center bottom weight, whose yellow twisted ribbons are speckled with aventurine copper scales. Like some crowns, it has a small hole in the bottom, this one made by drilling, perhaps to smooth out a perforated pontil mark. The color twist rims of the shot cups are attractive.

PLATE 32

The shot cup pair at top left and right is interesting because the members in the paperweight base, instead of being vertical, are curved as in swirl paperweights, perhaps in this instance to complement the threads in the bowls. Miniatures like the weight at bottom right are uncommon.

HAND COOLERS

If the romantic notion has it that hand coolers were made to cool ladies' hands for kissing or holding, evidence also shows that a few were used as darning eggs.

PLATE 33

Except for the scrambled Saint-Louis weight at top left, the other hand coolers were blown and are therefore hollow. This one is remarkable for being dated "S. L. 1845," the earliest date appearing on a Saint-Louis or indeed on any French paperweight. It also contains canes that do not appear in later millefiori. The other examples show typical overlay work, especially the floral-fruit cutting of the weight at bottom left, which also appears on lizard weights, plates, and vases from that factory.

FLOWERS

Unlike the millefiori in paperweights illustrated up to this point, flowers are made and assembled in a process known as lampwork, in which clear and colored glass rods are heated in a burner flame so that they may be manipulated and tooled to form stems, leaves, and flower petals, and fused together to form flowers. Paperweight flowers are more symbolic than realistic and their names must be taken loosely.

PLATE 34

Pansies from all three factories grace this page. The Baccarat weight, top left, is the standard, most common pansy, with its set arrangement of leaves and precise delineation of the flower. Hundreds of these were made, but this one is elaborately engraved with the initials "JWF," undoubtedly a presentation piece. The Baccarat weight, bottom center, shows lower crow's-foot petals with serrated edges, a less popular version made during the same years as the

standard pansy. The Clichy and Saint-Louis pansies, bottom left and top right, are more like violas and less frequently seen. The Baccarat weight in the center on lace ground is a remarkable though not entirely successful performance. Underneath, the lace ground is stuffed with colored filigree.

PLATE 35

Five clematis weights give a good idea of the varied approaches to this common paperweight flower. The typical amber-flash ground is a good foil for the blue flower in the center Saint-Louis weight, while the pale yellow petals of the Baccarat weight, top left, are made of opaque white rods shaped to a point and coated with translucent amber. The pink striping of the Saint-Louis weight, top right, along with its bud, makes this example particularly attractive. The sulphurous flower centers, bottom left and bottom right, help identify Saint-Louis as the maker. The Saint-Louis weight, bottom right, with two flowers on a color ground, is rare.

PLATE 36

Two of the Saint-Louis flowers at top right and bottom right are on jasper grounds, the green and white jasper at top right being particularly fine-grained. Two others, bottom left and center, have rare green aventurine grounds, with spiral torsades indenting the grounds while the flowers lie flush. Much more conservative, the Baccarat white clematis, top left, rests in clear glass within a ring of canes over a well-cut basal star.

PLATE 37

Six flowers from Baccarat show characteristic austerity. All have star-cut bases but, except for one ring of canes, and faceting on four weights, no other adornment. The clematis weights, top left, center left, and bottom left, make a delightful trio, though the faceting on the first is not original. The weight at bottom right is related to flowers on Plate 38.

PLATE 38

These symbolic flowers, again from Baccarat, are standardized. Each has the same number and arrangement of leaves, while the two long lower leaves of the weight at top right are associated with miniature and certain other floral examples. The Gothic-Moorish petals of the bottom center weight and the one right of center are ridged. It is interesting to note that the various parts of the flower are fused by lampwork: the main stem does not support the central cane from behind; it does not extend that far. The flower petals support the flower center. In other flowers the stem *does* appear to support the petals.

PLATE 39

Closed clematis or perhaps periwinkle buds from Baccarat show the care with which the stems were intertwined in a pattern obviously thought to enhance this simple subject. The table-cut weight at the top has, unusually, both pink and white buds. These flowers have sometimes been referred to as tulips.

PLATE 40

The colorful dahlia-related flowers on this plate all happen to be from Saint-Louis, though Clichy also made a few. The petals begin as parallel rods brought together at the ends. As with the Baccarat pansies, the dark stripes on the amber weight, bottom left, were applied over a clear glass coating of the petals. The petals of the center left weight are actually multicolored and appear to fill the glass dome of the weight. The reds in the weights at top right and bottom right would be hard to duplicate today.

PLATE 41

The three pom-poms on the left are from Saint-Louis, who specialized in latticinio grounds, while those on the right are from Baccarat, who made fewer and occasionally circled the flower with canes. The Saint-Louis weights at top left and center left reverse the flower and ground colors. Saint-Louis favored feathery blossoms, while the white flower in the bottom left weight looks more like the Baccarat examples. Like their American counterparts, Saint-Louis pom-poms often indent their grounds, imparting a wave to the latticinio. In the bottom left weight the tomato coloring of the ground is achieved with a translucent coating of red glass above and beneath the opaque white latticinio, rather than a color coating of the individual latticinio strands.

PLATE 42

At the top of the plate the weights at left and right are attractive but atypical Baccarat floral fantasies and, as such, rather rare. The Saint-Louis blue dahlia, bottom left, has the dome and window faceting frequently used by Saint-Louis for this flower.

PLATE 43

A variety of roses from all three factories graces this plate. The center weight is tilted to show the petals of a typical Clichy rose. Clichy seldom used the latticinio ground and then only for flowers. Three well-formed Baccarat roses and a Saint-Louis dog rose, top left, on latticinio complete the group.

PLATE 44

A Baccarat blue buttercup, top right, and a pink fringed gentian, bottom left. Balanced by two Saint-Louis fuchsias, one, top left, a rarity with two blossoms. The topmost bud in fuchsias doubles as a cherry in the Saint-Louis fruit weights. Like the Baccarat roses in the preceding plate, these semirealistic flowers are among the more successful floral efforts.

PLATE 45

The Clichy weight at the top is one of a limited number of examples, perhaps because as a design it was considered somewhat bland. The bottom weight is a stunning imaginary flower from the Val-Saint-Lambert factory in Belgium, who made few flower weights. The petals are laminated with colored stripes, an idea possibly suggested by the Baccarat primrose. Typically, a twisted ribbon encloses the design; the flat base is star cut.

PLATE 46

About the time of the Exposition Universelle, 1878, in Paris, there was a glass paperweight revival that stressed designs in three-dimensional relief, and these two striking roses from an undetermined source, perhaps the Pantin factory, may date from that time. The phosphorescent yellow flower centers and the leaf serrations suggest Saint-Louis, but the leaf coloring and the light bubbly glass do not. Wherever they were made they are Victorian workmanship at its best.

PLATE 47

Another rose in relief, but this one sits in a pocket of air, for this unknown French weight, possibly from Saint-Louis, is hollow blown. Two other examples are known to the author.

PLATE 48

Three more flowers of undetermined origin. The top weight shows certain resemblances to Saint-Louis, while the bottom weight resembles flowers in the great lizard weights. The cutting on the center weight as well as the tricolored petals and heavy glass all suggest Saint-Louis.

FLAT FLORAL BOUQUETS

These include all flower groups that lie flat and have, basically, two dimensions. In some instances the flowers are represented by canes.

PLATE 49

The striking Baccarat clematis and pansy bouquet, top, and the lovely Saint-Louis arrangement, bottom right, appear a number of times with different flowers and coloring, but the floral cornucopia from Clichy, bottom left, was never a regular pattern and may be considered extremely rare.

PLATE 50

Three impressive magnums from Baccarat with buttercup centers and star-cut bases. The varied use of arrow rods in each is interesting, especially the red arrow rods in the weight at top right and the green arrow rods inside the white in the one at top left. All flowers and leaves lie flat except the buttercup, which deeply indents the design level.

PLATE 51

Two very beautiful floral bouquets from Clichy showing in more casual arrangement the natural leafage and fluid lampwork of that factory. In the bottom weight the striped pink petals are actually canes sliced open lengthwise, while the luscious bouquet in the top weight is tied around the stems with a white ribbon.

PLATE 52

Two more Clichy bouquets: the one top left on latticinio with a Clichy rose and again tied with a white ribbon, and the other, top right, with a blue flower whose petals are actually canes, tied this time with a pink ribbon. More formal in appearance is the Baccarat set piece, bottom left, of three red clematis with long symmetrical lower leaves. A strong Clichy influence, particularly in the flowers and the ground of parallel filigree strands, is seen in the weight at bottom right, possibly from Val-Saint-Lambert or Venice. There is also an encircling garland of Clichy-like roses, but accompanied, perhaps uniquely, by goldstone leaves. The most Belgian features are the torsade (invisible from the top) and the flat base. The glass, though typically light in weight, is of good clarity.

PLATE 53

In another type of flat floral bouquet the flowers are represented by canes (usually four) on leaves (usually five) and stem. Saint-Louis made most of these, often with an amber-flashed background as in the weight at bottom left, sometimes also diamond cut as in the one at top right. The center weight is probably an early one made before leaf arrangements and serrations were finally determined. Use of a single cane as in the gorgeously cut miniature, bottom center, is extremely rare.

PLATE 54

This massive weight is a puzzle: though it centers a typical Saint-Louis clematis and the faceting is in Saint-Louis style, it also contains some Clichy-like canes, including white roses, and the long parallel filigree rods underneath the ground that one associates with Clichy. The glass, though heavy, is not of Saint-Louis or Clichy quality.

UPRIGHT BOUQUETS

These are three-dimensional versions of the flat bouquet with canes and small flowers set among the vertical sprays of leaves.

PLATE 55

Six examples from Saint-Louis showing the upright bouquet nesting in a variety of torsades in red, white, and blue. The striped effect of the broad torsades in the weights at top left and center recalls the Clichy swirl. At bottom right is a hand cooler with a double-headed bouquet. The small weight, center right, may originally have been a stopper or seal.

PLATE 56

Four upright bouquets, including a rare one, bottom left, from Baccarat, who seldom made this form. The pink torsade here, though wobbly in the glass dome, is masterfully done. Saint-Louis frequently made an all-white torsade, as in the one at top right.

PLATE 57

Yellow torsades as in this Saint-Louis weight are seldom seen. Notice how the concave punties multiply both torsade and leaves—intentionally, of course.

PLATE 58

A Saint-Louis red over white double overlay with upright bouquet, but this spectacular and extremely rare example is not further encased. Note the beautifully centered bouquet and the brilliant effect of the star-cut base echoed in each window.

PLATE 59

These remarkable encased overlays from Saint-Louis also contain upright bouquets. In the complicated encased overlay process, the casing, or overlay, had to be cooled in the annealing oven *(lehr)* before the windows could be cut. Then the weight had to be carefully reheated and covered with a further coating of clear glass, a multiple operation that must have taken days to complete. Examples like those illustrated here are infrequently seen, but the elaborate cutting of the overlay in the center weight, to reveal within oval panels a hare and two hounds, makes it a triumph of paperweight-making. For sheer color the blue overlay at bottom right is especially brilliant.

FRUITS

Plates 60 through 64 indicate the range of French fruit paperweights, from arrangements that employ the latticinio basket to those that rely on faceting to multiply a simple image.

PLATE 60

Six typical Saint-Louis fruits in latticinio baskets. Except for the formally arranged turnips in the weight at top left, the fruits in the other weights appear to have been strewn casually as one might actually see them in a basket or bowl. The latticinio, bottom right, resembles a lace doily.

PLATE 61

Three more fruits in latticinio baskets contrasted with three miniature fruits in clear glass. Faceting and the large shaded and striped pear, bottom right, make this an unusual and attractive weight.

PLATE 62

Easily the most spectacular of the fruit weights and one of the finest weights in the Sinclair Collection is this flawlessly made, natural-looking pear with twig and leaves on a brilliant vermilion ground, with a probable Clichy attribution. Color, placement—everything works together in this striking design.

PLATE 63

The top and bottom weights show the typical Saint-Louis strawberry design of two fruits, one fully ripe, and the white strawberry flower on latticinio ground; but the latter is unusual in that the latticinio ground is single ply and swirled. By contrast the Baccarat example at left shows us three spherical strawberries, one convincingly unripe. The red dots on the surface of the berries are actually the centers of thin hexagonal rods.

PLATE 64

Grapes, plums, and cherries in facetings that multiply the fruit. Note the successful attempts at top left and bottom left to suggest grape leaves, not to mention the tiny grapes.

FAUNA

With Plates 65 through 71, we enter the world of nature's creatures that so fascinated the Frenchman of the period. One thinks of the interest in zoos and of the anthropomorphic fantasies of Grandville. In paperweights it was the heyday of animal silhouettes, of butterflies and lizards.

PLATE 65

Four Baccarat butterflies, two of them hovering over white clematis, the other two within a circle of canes. The bodies are mauve filigree canes and the upper wing markings are slices of cane. In the center of the plate is a miniature paperweight seal, its top hexagonal with a close-set bunch of flowers, its base bearing in the Cyrillic alphabet the words "Kramer, Smolensk" about the Gothic initials "C.N." or "C.W." The top and stem appear to have been mated with a wafer of white glass after manufacture.

PLATE 66

Two more Baccarat butterflies, the flat faceted one at top of brilliant glass showing the lepidopter over a finely made white clematis in a moment of arrested nature.

PLATE 67

Though the four butterflies in the corners of this plate imitate the Baccarat butterfly and the canes in the wings of one appear to be Baccarat canes, the glass of these weights is very light in the hand, the bases are flat yet show little wear, and the basal stars are crudely cut. Nor do the slightly lurid colors suggest a Victorian provenance. The center one, an enameled butterfly seen in profile, has the look and coloring of china decoration in the first decades of the 20th century.

PLATE 68

These herpetological creatures coiled on their beds of jasper, sand, and lace are from Baccarat and Saint-Louis. The cutting on the weights at top left and right is similar to that on the Baccarat sulphides of Joan of Arc (see Plate 78) and others.

PLATE 69

Animal figures are all extremely rare from any source. At the top are two early Saint-Louis subjects, the squirrel, left, and the fanciful bird, right, each with diamond-cut base and a delicate torsade that cannot be seen from the top. The figures show the early difficulties with precise lampwork and the less effective image created by the flattened dome. The weight at bottom is a transfer of a rather embryonic-looking horse on a ceramic ground within a ring of typical Baccarat canes, valuable chiefly because of its rarity.

PLATE 70

The lampworked "Swans in the Pond," bottom left, and the similar "Ducks in the Pond," bottom right, often attributed to Baccarat, are hollow-blown weights, with the birds fused to the algae-ringed bases. By contrast, the equally rare Saint-Louis sulphide carp at the top float in solid glass, one over a jasper ground.

PLATE 71

Lizards modeled in three-dimensional relief decorate the tops of paperweights that appear to be hollow blown, probably in a mold, since the diameters of all three are identical. All are from Saint-Louis and all are gilded. At bottom is one of faceted opaline glass with the gilding between the facets, while the center one is of green and white jasper similar to the ground of the weight, bottom right, in Plate 68.

SULPHIDES

From the early years of the nineteenth century in France clay cameos, called sulphides, of historical figures were incrusted (embedded) in all sorts of glass objects from bottles to candlesticks. In the 1840s and up until the beginning of the Second Empire in 1852, sulphide paperweights were popular, though far fewer sulphides than other types of paperweights were made. French sulphides (Plates 72 through 81) included portraits of English and American as well as French personages.

PLATE 72

Three fine sulphides of King Louis Philippe, Napoleon, and Lafayette, with a silvery look imparted to the white clay by the thin pocket of air between the cameo and the enclosing glass. The deep translucent aquamarine ground of the Louis Philippe weight at the top is unusual and effective, as is the sunburst cutting of the translucent cranberry ground at bottom left. The translucent ultramarine blue ground, bottom right, has as much life as the sulphide of Lafayette.

PLATE 73

Except for the Baccarat portrait of the older Lafayette on a translucent lime green ground in the center, all the fine sulphides in this group are on opaque grounds. By the time they were made in the late 1840s all the subjects but Wellington, the one at bottom left by Baccarat, were memories. The rich cerulean grounds were typical of Clichy.

PLATE 74

These portraits of Victoria show the queen in four different sulphide treatments, of which the earliest is perhaps the round medallion, bottom left, which commemorates, in addition to her birth and coronation, her marriage on February 10, 1840. The faceting Clichy reserved for some of its finer weights is given the handsome portrait on deep amethyst ground, at top left. In many portraits, as in the one at bottom right, Victoria appears with Albert.

PLATE 75

All the sulphides here are portraits of Louis Napoleon Bonaparte and, except for the amber-flashed examples from Saint-Louis (center and top center), all are presumably from Baccarat. The future emperor Napoleon III (1852–1870) was in and out of the limelight for many years previously, returning to France as president after the Revolution of 1848, which may account for the aging revealed in these sulphide likenesses taken, as were most sulphides, from medals.

PLATE 76

A variety of sulphide subjects with, at the top, a Baccarat likeness of William II, framed in a laurel wreath tied with a red ribbon. William II was king of the Netherlands and grand duke of Luxembourg (1840–1849). Another profile of Louis Napoleon from Saint-Louis, top left, rests within a ring of canes over a diamond-cut ground. At the bottom right from Clichy is a fine sulphide of General Zachary Taylor on a translucent forest green ground with a typical ring of canes. The rarest sulphide here, in the center, from an unknown source, perhaps Allen and Moore, shows Prince Albert. The medallion delicately bordered in oak and laurel must have been difficult to incrust without breaking.

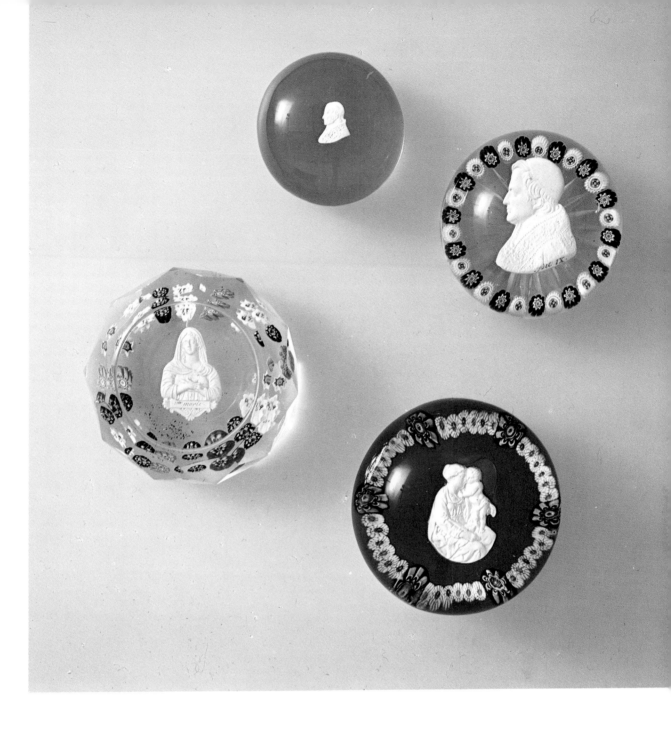

PLATE 77

These religious sulphide subjects include two profiles (top and top right) of Pope Pius IX —both from Saint-Louis—a Sainte Marie by Clichy (left) with an unusual cutting treatment, and another Clichy (bottom right) with a lovely sulphide of a mother and child, again within the typical ring of canes.

PLATE 78

Baccarat was partial to translucent cranberry or ruby for some of its more exotic sulphides. The meticulously incrusted sulphide of Joan of Arc, bottom, her helmet resting on the stump of a tree, is particularly effective against ruby but also appears against blue, green, and clear glass.

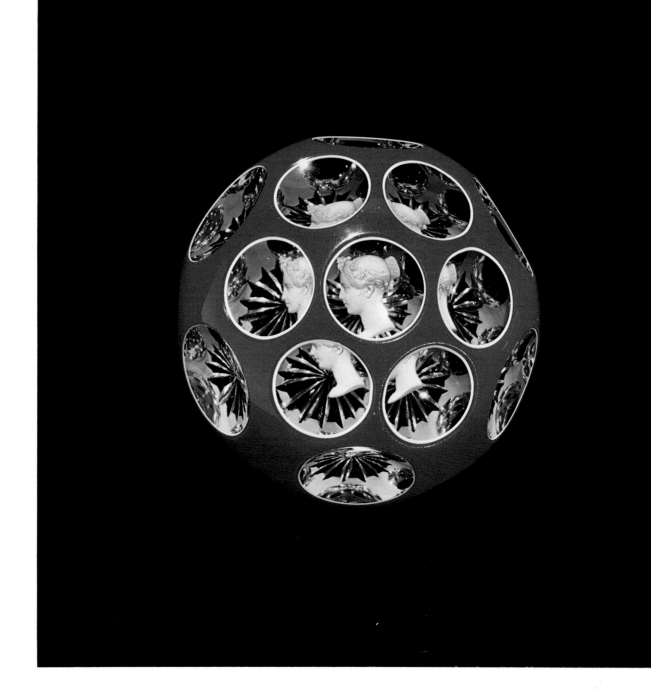

PLATE 79

A superb magnum double overlay from Baccarat enclosing a sulphide portrait of the young Queen Victoria. The careful placing and deep precise cutting of the twenty-five punties to reveal glimpses of the portrait and the star-cut base, and the pantheonic dome effect of the inner opaque white casing, achieve a result both rich and restrained.

PLATE 80

Though sulphide cameos were enclosed by glass as early as 1798, these wall plaques in neoclassic style were probably made after 1820. The plaque at top left contains a clay cameo of Czar Alexander I of Russia, bearing the signature of the medalist Andrieu, from whose mold it was perhaps taken by Desprez. The sharp strawberry diamond cutting of the base is reminiscent of both French and Anglo-Irish neoclassic decoration. Washington, at bottom left, is a cameo by Martoret from the Duvivier medal; while the Napoleon plaque, bottom right, is perhaps by Desprez for Baccarat. The rectangular plaque with diamond-cut base at top right, perhaps by Baccarat, appears to represent the Duc de Berry of France. The medals included (top center and center) are probably of later date.

PLATE 81

The main body of this rare Clichy letterweight bears a sulphide portrait of Louis Napoleon and is surmounted by a knob in the form of a miniature spaced concentric weight. Note the protruding oval medallions of glass in typical Clichy style and the relief diamond cutting of base and shoulders, a form carried over from the 1820s and 1830s. This is not an inkwell or bottle, but a solid glass paperweight.

MIXED MEDIA WEIGHTS

Plates 82 through 86 present a sampling of secondary techniques applied to paper-weight-making, including painting, intaglio cutting, and repoussé.

PLATE 82

Two unusual faceted weights from Baccarat or Saint-Louis whose bases are etched through an amber flash: one, bottom, a labeled portrait of Empress Eugénie, the other, top, with a pointing hound in a rural setting. Acid reverse etching through the flashing has left a frosted appearance on the clear glass, while giving the amber lines of the pictures the quality of engraving.

PLATE 83

The two painted weights at the right are probably Bohemian. They are extremely light in the hand but not, apparently, hollow blown, and both are deeply star cut to the perimeter of the base. The floral example, bottom right, is punty cut above the base, while the butterfly example, top right, is gilded in the same area. These factors suggest a Bohemian origin. The large weight at the left, showing two putti—one with bow and arrow, the other with doves and roses—was painted on a slightly convex porcelain plaque in the 19th-century manner and is undoubtedly European.

PLATE 84

The design of this remarkable paperweight—leaves and berries—is intaglio-cut through a quadruple-cased ground of white over green, over white over ruby red, and the weight in turn overlaid in white. A vase by Bacchus of Birmingham with similar color layering and cut design appears in the *Art-Journal Crystal Palace Exhibition Illustrated Catalogue,* 1851 (see Fig. 3, p. 12), so perhaps this is from Bacchus.

PLATE 85

Three fine Pinchbecks with figured scenes executed in repoussé technique. At bottom a couple appear on horseback accompanied by a dog. Gold and silver Pinchbeck metal combine skillfully here to delineate the scene. At top is a domestic scene in silver Pinchbeck metal that might be titled "The Singing Lesson," while the metal in the center weight has been painted to enhance a pastoral dancing scene.

PLATE 86

Typically, these Pinchbecks present a variety of religious and secular scenes taken from paintings or engravings. The one at the top shows Christ crowned with thorns, while at the bottom right is an equestrian camp scene in the costume of Louis XIII. Because they are ingeniously constructed and the subjects are difficult to see, the covering lenses of these Pinchbeck paperweights have been removed for this illustration.

CONTINENTAL AND ENGLISH MILLEFIORI

It seems appropriate here, as a bridge to American paperweight-making, to show some of the millefiori not included with the earlier plates.

PLATE 87

Two Bohemian spaced millefiori paperweights on lace grounds topped by vases overlaid and cut in the Bohemian style of the 1840s. The taller vase bears on its base a paper label and the words in inked script "Purchased in Paris, France, by a prominent Bostonian in 1847"; while the paperweight of the smaller vase has several silhouette canes and is dated. The double overlay on the vase itself is interesting, for the inner ruby casing appears on the inner surface of the vase and is separated from the outer white overlay by a casing of clear glass.

PLATE 88

A large flat-bottomed Belgian paperweight, probably from Val-Saint-Lambert, is double overlaid in translucent chartreuse yellow over translucent pink, giving the overlay a dichroic appearance. A blue and white glass or clay medallion in the center of the design reads: "NICOLAS FASTRE INGENIEUR HONORAIRE DES MINES." The canes of the concentric arrangement about the medallion are extremely delicate in construction and coloring.

PLATE 89

Like most millefiori from the English factory of Whitefriars in London, the inkwell with stopper seen here is a concentric and dated 1848. The two weights at bottom, also dated and from Whitefriars, are low domed.

PLATE 90

Another Whitefriars inkwell with stopper dated 1848, and a concentric from the Bacchus factory, bottom. The only date appearing in Whitefriars paperweights of the Classic period is 1848, while Bacchus weights are not dated at all.

PLATE 91

A rare and beautiful weight from George Bacchus & Sons of Birmingham, England, with panels of red and white canes within "sodden snow" rings about a large central ruffled cane. A perimeter of blue-lined, white cogged canes completes the elegantly simple, almost Georgian motif.

PLATE 92

Two green bottle glass weights and a doorstop made by bottle factories in various parts of England after 1829. Though in point of date these may be the earliest paperweights made, they were as often used to line garden paths or to drive nails into walls as to hold down paper. The projectile-shaped weight at left, with its tiered flowers sprouting from a flowerpot, has been made from the early days and is perhaps still being made. The foot is a late development.

AMERICAN PAPERWEIGHTS

The Great Exhibition of 1851 in London and the exhibition two years later in New York brought Continental and English paperweights before the American public. American gaffers were usually men born and trained in Europe. Thus American paperweights are often based upon European prototypes, particularly the French. Paperweights in the French manner continued to be produced in the United States through 1880, long after Classic paperweight-making had ceased in France. At the turn of the century, in southern New Jersey, new upright forms appeared, made with a crimp, in the first distinct break with European tradition.

PLATE 93

Two New England Glass Co. red over white double overlays elaborately faceted in the Bohemian manner, an influence especially noted at the Crystal Palace Exhibition of 1853. The interior motifs are concentrics, the one at the top centering a rabbit silhouette.

PLATE 94

This is the only paperweight in the society's collections from Gillinder & Sons of Philadelphia and one of the few carpet grounds from that factory, which made mostly concentrics. Like other weights, it has the characteristic long, very deeply cut oval punties and the feathery canes formed as a dome. The lower rim of white canes draws to the center of the base in the Bacchus manner.

PLATE 95

In American paperweight-making the crown form derives from Saint-Louis. Those left and right center, with the colored ribbons in random sequence, are from the Boston & Sandwich Glass Co., while the color-balanced arrangements, top and bottom, are from the New England Glass Co. All are hollow blown and some have holes drilled in the bases, perhaps to round out perforated pontil marks.

PLATE 96

Of these flower weights the white poinsettia, bottom right, from Sandwich, is the commonest, while the orchid coloring of the petals of the one at left and the cool pink ground of the center weight are rare in American paperweights. Note the resemblance of the blue flower petals in this center example to Saint-Louis clematis petals of the same color, as shown in Plate 35.

PLATE 97

A pink pom-pom (left) and a white pom-pom (top) in the Saint-Louis manner from Cambridge. Telltale strands of latticinio and the similar small size indicate the weights were made either as a pair or consecutively. The large bubbles that punctuate the pink petals of the weight at the right give sparkle to this beautifully assembled and typically off-center Sandwich flower. In the bottom weight the flower set flush with a fine-textured pink jasper ground is modeled on the Baccarat buttercup.

PLATE 98

A group of New England Glass Co. designs made from glass leaves and petals. The cross motifs, top left and top right, are backed and apparently held together by green stems not visible from the top. These austere designs are typically American.

PLATE 99

The white mushroom-shaped ground of this superb cocoa over white double overlay from the New England Glass Co. centers a flat bouquet in Saint-Louis style with canes for flowers, and an outer ring of finely formed canes in alternating colors. The masterful cutting, including small clover cuts, again shows the Bohemian influence, seen also in American overlaid lamp fonts.

PLATE 100

Upright bouquets in red, white, and blue from the New England Glass Co., all of which rest in latticinio baskets. The bottom weight shows two realistic lampworked roses and bud placed over a finely woven latticinio ground—a rare and wonderful paperweight.

PLATE 101

The magnum at top shows the brilliant coloring and careful placement of the best American lampwork. Note the two small fruits among the leaves and flowers. The lovely colors of the circular spray at bottom are further enhanced by a Saint-Louis style of hollow diamond cutting that appears to be original and was perhaps done to hide the sugary glass. Despite the sugar, the paperweight is rich and exciting.

PLATE 102

Lampwork of the quality evident in this three-dimensional floral spray equals the finest in French paperweight lampwork. The stems of the precise sparkling flowers are bound in the Clichy manner with a ribbon. The neat latticinio ground and the flat triangular faceting of this magnum weight, which repeats the points of petals and leaves, are part of the unified ensemble.

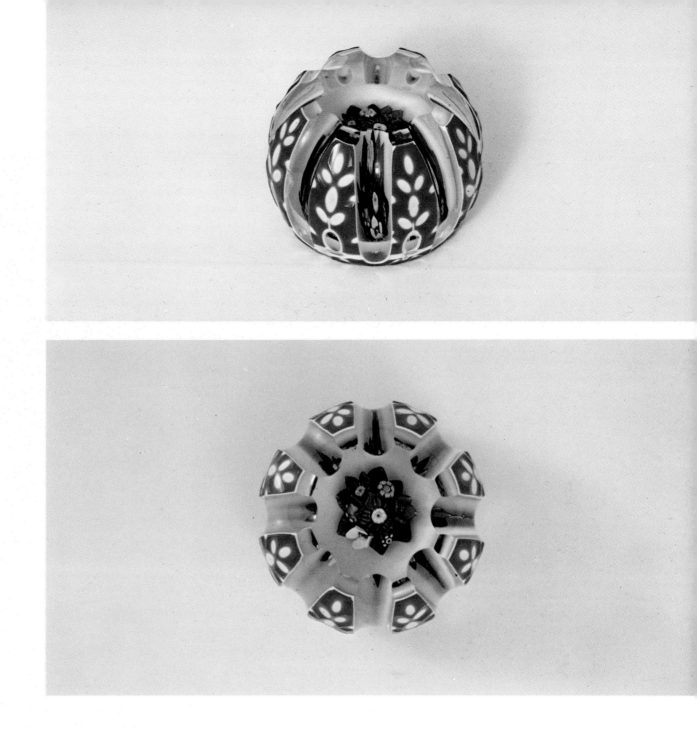

PLATE 103

A rare example of the glass cutter's skill is this double overlay seen here in top and side views. The raspberry over white overlay is cut in long vertical flutes to reveal the upright bouquet. The remaining overlay panels are further cut, but only to the white layer, to suggest leaves. The ground in which the bouquet rests is a white bowl whose sides come up just far enough to create the illusion of an all-white interior surface. An extraordinary blending of skills within a unified concept is evident here.

PLATE 104

One can easily imagine the lampwork process from the shaping of the mottled rose petals, bottom. Typical of Mt. Washington Glass Co. work are the acid green of the leaves and stem, and on the base the waffle pattern left from the pontil rod gather of glass, which had been pressed into a waffle or crisscross mold to ease the separation of the paperweight when it was cracked off the rod. Another Mt. Washington characteristic is the vertical bundling of petals seen in the salmon-colored dahlia, top, suggesting a flower not completely opened.

PLATE 105

A realistic life-size rose fills this Mt. Washington magnum weight, perhaps the largest single piece of paperweight lampwork from an American factory. It has audacity.

PLATE 106

Three extremely rare lampwork performances from the New England Glass Co. that are on a par with similar French work (see Plate 69). Like the roses in the center weight, the head and body of the parrot, bottom, were achieved by trailing. Such weights may have been made as gifts or as tests of skill, but are too scarce to have been part of regular production.

PLATE 107

When compared to those from Saint-Louis (Plates 60, 61, 63, and 64), the fruit arrangements on this plate are symmetrical and formal. The flat spray of berries, at bottom right, from Sandwich or the New England Glass Co., shows an unground pontil mark, which probably indicates that it too was not a production item.

PLATE 108

There is a folk-art feeling about these pink cherries and blue plums from Sandwich. By contrast the strawberries with blossoms in the rare magnum from Mt. Washington, top, look real enough to eat.

PLATE 109

A blown apple, an apricot, and two pears on "cookie" bases from the New England Glass Co., whose specialty these were. The blown white fruit is said to have been partially dipped in pots of different colored glass, reheated to bleed the colors, and finally fused to the base. The blossom ends show the pontil mark where the fruit was held to the pontil rod. Note the realistic striping on the fine large apple, bottom left.

PLATE 110

Four more blown fruits from the New England Glass Co. Blown fruits were also made at Saint-Louis, but the bases were rectangular and more elaborately modeled to suggest napery. The coloring of these American fruits is particularly fresh.

PLATE III

It is difficult to determine the sources of these sulphides. The double portrait of Victoria and Albert, bottom right, was perhaps made by Clichy at the time of the Great Exhibition, and the sulphide cameos themselves may be French or English. But the glass of these weights looks American. The popularity of General Zachary Taylor as a sulphide subject (center) stems from his victory over Santa Anna at Buena Vista in 1847, during the Mexican War, a victory that made him president.

PLATE 112

With these roses and the water lily from Whitall Tatum & Co. of Millville, New Jersey, we enter the early years of the 20th century and the new era of the crimp, a metal mold with a handle that transformed a gather of colored glass into a flower in one skilled movement. The saffron yellow rose without leaves is rare enough, but the spectacular water lily, with its tuberous pink and yellow center, its white petals and green leaves, is seen even less often. All three weights pictured here have footed bases.

PLATE 113

Except for the delicate opal pink rose, top right, which has a flat base, the rose weights here are footed. Millville roses were made by four well-known gaffers, including Ralph Barber, who was born in England. The bright yellow, top left, and the apricot color, bottom left, are unusual and arresting.

PLATE 114

The white Millville rose with the pale green leaves is not footed but has a flat frosted base. The footed bases of the other three roses show the pontil mark, and the pontil mark on the bottom right weight is X-shaped. The small pink rose, bottom left, was made by the great modern paperweight artist Charles Kaziun after 1940.

PLATE 115

A full-blown red rose, probably made by Ralph Barber, is tilted in a limpid glass sphere above a baluster stem and foot at right. The solid harmonious proportions of the ensemble could not be improved upon. The crocus streaked with colored glass and goldstone above a conical pedestal base, at left, was probably made before 1920 and perhaps by Charles Pepper at Whitall Tatum & Co. or at the T. C. Wheaton Co., both in Millville.

PLATE 116

Flat upright designs from Millville are shown on this and the following plate. The cross in the wilderness, at right, perhaps made by Michael Kane of Whitall Tatum, is also cut in Millville style with five deep circular punties. The picture was made by brushing powdered colored glass into the design engraved on a steel die. By contrast with Millville work in the weight at left a flat pink poinsettia is placed in a flattened sphere above a hollow baluster stem and foot. Possibly it is a Nicholas Lutz creation from his later years at Mt. Washington or at the Union Glass Co. in Somerville, Massachusetts. The flower is not as easy to see as the upright Millville flowers.

PLATE 117

Michael Kane may also have made these two steel-die pictures from Millville. The horse at right and the sloop at left, which may be viewed from either side, have an American primitive look, as if the objects were taken from nineteenth-century folk painting. Perhaps the sailing sloop was meant to represent the *Spray,* in which Captain Joshua Slocum started around the world in 1895, though the boat, formerly an oyster sloop, was rigged as a yawl for the voyage.

PLATE 118

Two massive weights from the Union Glass Co. of Somerville, Massachusetts, probably made before 1920, the one at bottom with three lampwork pigs and blossoms on a mottled ground, the one at top with two birds at a nest containing three eggs. The subjects are crudely done, but the fine lead glass, typical of Somerville, is free of bubbles and striae.

PLATE 119

A footed Tiffany paperweight of doorstop size, showing two diaphanous, three-dimensional, lettuce green fish swimming among long streamers of faintly iridescent aquatic material. The pale bottle green of the enclosing glass completes the watery illusion. The foot is signed. Only about a dozen glass paperweights by Tiffany are known.

PLATE 120

These modern paperweights on darkly colored grounds are typical of Paul Ysart or his workshop in the 1940s or 1950s. Though styled in the Victorian lampwork manner, these designs lack the refinement of Classic period lampwork. The flowers at bottom are tied with a red aventurine ribbon.

PART THREE

CATALOGUE

KEY TO CATALOGUE SYMBOLS

AU   Austria
B   Baccarat (Compagnie des Cristalleries de Baccarat)
BF   bottle factory
BO   Bohemia
BS   Bacchus (George Bacchus & Sons)
C   Clichy (Clichy-la-Garenne)
CH   China
CZ   Czechoslovakia
E   England
EU   Europe
F   France
G   Gillinder & Sons, Philadelphia
GE   Germany
M   Whitall Tatum & Co., Millville, New Jersey
MW   Mt. Washington Glass Co., New Bedford, Mass.
NE   New England Glass Co., East Cambridge, Mass.
P   Pinchbeck
S   Boston & Sandwich Glass Co., Sandwich, Mass.
SL   Saint-Louis (Compagnie des Cristalleries de Saint-Louis)
SO   Union Glass Co., Somerville, Mass.
T   Tiffany (L. C. Tiffany, Favrile)
U   undetermined origin
US   America
V   Vasart Co., Perth, Scotland
VL   Val-Saint-Lambert, Seraing, Belgium
W   Whitefriars (James Powell & Sons, Whitefriars, London)
Y   Paul Ysart, Scotland

COLOR PLATES

PLATE 1

1965.224.SL (A), (B) *(top)* France, Saint-Louis, c. 1845–50.
Pair of wafer dishes on scrambled paperweight bases, the ruffled rims edged in cobalt blue. High lead content.
Height 3 1/4″ (8.3 cm.); diam. 2 5/8″ (6.7 cm.)

1965.102.SL (A), (B) *(center)* France, Saint-Louis, c. 1845–50.
Pair of shot cups with miniature scrambled paperweight bases, the horizontally threaded bowls also decorated with spiral filigree rods alternating with blue rods.
Height 3 7/16″ (8 cm.); diam. about 1 3/4″ (4.4 cm.)

1939.45.B *(bottom left)* France, Baccarat, 1845–50.
Scrambled paperweight, the short length of brightly colored filigree canes set at right angles.
Diam. 2 1/2″ (6.3 cm.)

1939.86.C *(bottom right)* France, Clichy, c. 1845–50.
Scrambled weight with a jumble of brightly colored canes.
Diam. 2 9/16″ (6.5 cm.)

PLATE 2

1965.305.C *(top left)* France, Clichy, c. 1845–50.
Miniature close millefiori with roses in white stave basket.
Diam. 1 3/4″ (4.4 cm.)

1965.119.B *(top right)* France, Baccarat, 1847.
Close millefiori with two figure canes and dated "B. 1947."
Diam. 2 1/8″ (5.4 cm.)

1965.320.B *(center)* France, Baccarat, 1848.
Wafer dish with close millefiori paperweight base dated "B. 1848," the bowl engraved with rosebushes and with a spiral-ribboned rim in red, white, and blue.
Height 3 3/4″ (9.6 cm.); diam. 3 1/4″ (8.3 cm.)

1965.153.C *(bottom left)* France, Clichy, c. 1845–50.
Close millefiori with roses and one cane signed "C." All in a cerulean blue and white stave basket.
Diam. 2 9/16″ (6.5 cm.)

1965.258.B *(bottom right)* France, Baccarat, c. 1845–50.
Close millefiori with Clichy-like roses and the usual Baccarat canes.
Diam. 2 1/2″ (6.3 cm.)

PLATE 3

1965.170.C *(top left)* France, Clichy, c. 1845–50.
Close millefiori with numerous roses in white stave basket.
Diam. 2 3/4″ (7 cm.)

1965.155.B *(top right)* France, Baccarat, 1847.
Close millefiori with figure canes, one dated "B. 1847."
Diam. 3 1/8″ (7.9 cm.)

1965.359.C *(center)* France, Clichy, c. 1845–50.
Close millefiori with roses and one cane signed "C" in red, in a deep purple and white stave basket.
Diam. 2 11/16″ (6.8 cm.)

1965.111.C *(bottom left)* France, Clichy, c. 1845–50.
Close millefiori with numerous roses and white stave basket, one cane signed "C."
Diam. 2 5/8" (6.7 cm.)

1965.293.C *(bottom right)* France, Clichy, mid-19th century.
Close millefiori, with one cane signed "C" in blue, in a white and cerulean blue stave basket.
No roses. Reground.
Diam. 2 7/8" (7.3 cm.)

PLATE 4

1952.188.B *(top)* France, Baccarat, 1847.
Spaced millefiori on upset muslin ground with figure canes, one cane dated "B. 1847."
Diam. 3 1/8" (7.9 cm.)

1965.295.SL *(left)* France, Saint-Louis, c. 1845–50.
Spaced millefiori on upset muslin ground, with five green canes about a central cane, and an outer circle of alternately blue and chartreuse crow's-foot canes.
Diam. 2 3/4" (7 cm.)

1965.159.C *(right)* France, Clichy, c. 1845–50.
Newel-post or doorstop of magnum size, the spaced millefiori canes arranged in checker form on a domed grid of filigree canes with an underlayer of parallel filigree canes. Base ground flat and shows little wear.
Diam. 3 7/8" (9.9 cm.)

1939.83.C *(bottom)* France, Clichy, c. 1845–50.
Spaced concentric of two rows of bright canes about a central maroon, blue, and white cane on an upset muslin ground, one cane signed with a red "C."
Diam. 2 1/4" (5.7 cm.)

PLATE 5

1965.299.B *(top)* France, Baccarat, 1849.
Spaced millefiori with figure canes on muslin ground, one cane dated 1849. Reground.
Diam. 2 3/4" (7 cm.)

1965.381.SL *(center)* France, Saint-Louis, c. 1845–50.
Spaced millefiori of chartreuse canes about a salmon pink cane, all sunk in a blue and white jasper ground. Reground.
Diam. 3 3/4" (8.3 cm.)

1965.449.B *(left)* France, Baccarat, 1848.
Spaced millefiori concentric, upset lace ground, figure canes, one cane dated "B. 1848."
Diam. 2 5/8" (6.7 cm.)

1965.270.B *(right)* France, Baccarat, c. 1845–50.
Spaced millefiori with figure canes on lace ground. Reground.
Diam. 2 3/4" (7 cm.)

PLATE 6

1965.491.C France, Clichy, c. 1845–50.
Concentric circles of canes in blue, green, red, and white all contained in a pale, translucent sky blue and white stave basket, the next outer row of canes with thirteen Clichy roses.
Diam. 3 1/4" (8.3 cm.)

PLATE 7

1965.201.C *(top left)* France, Clichy, c. 1845–50.
Eight millefiori canes about a central Clichy rose.
Diam. 1 3/4″ (4.4 cm.)

1965.235.C *(top right)* France, Clichy, c. 1845–50.
Eight millefiori canes including a Clichy rose about a central ruffled pink cane.
Diam. 1 13/16″ (4.6 cm.)

1965.338.B *(center)* France, Baccarat, c. 1845–50.
Tulip shot cup with translucent blue overlay on the vertical edges above a millefiori concentric with four rows of typical canes about a central white stardust cane.
Height 4″ (10.2 cm.); diam. 2 5/8″ (6.7 cm.)

1939.96.C *(bottom left)* France, Clichy, c. 1845–50.
Miniature concentric with a ring of blue and a ring of alternately pink and green canes about a central Clichy rose.
Diam. 1 3/4″ (4.4 cm.)

1965.226.C *(bottom right)* France, Clichy, c. 1845–50.
Miniature concentric with a ring of pink and a ring of alternately green and white canes about a central blue cane.
Diam. 1 7/8″ (4.7 cm.)

PLATE 8

1939.89.B *(top)* France, Baccarat, c. 1845–50.
Miniature concentric with three rings of canes in red, white, and green about a central arrow cane.
Diam. 2″ (5.1 cm.)

1965.227.C *(top right)* France, Clichy, c. 1845–50.
Spaced concentric with two rings of lilac, and pink and green canes about a central pink and green rose, all on an upset muslin ground backed by parallel filigree canes.
Diam. 2 3/16″ (5.6 cm.)

1965.74.C *(left)* France, Clichy, c. 1845–50.
Spaced concentric in clear glass with three rows of white, purple, and green and pink canes including eighteen roses in groups of three. Cut with six punties and flat top facet. Base reground.
Diam. 2 3/4″ (7 cm.)

1965.377.C *(right)* France, Clichy, c. 1845–50.
A spaced concentric with three rings of blue, pink, lettuce green, and purple canes, about a central white cane. Refaceted with one top and six side punties. Base shows no wear.
Diam. 2 3/8″ (6 cm.)

1965.105.SL *(bottom)* France, Saint-Louis, c. 1845–50.
A close concentric millefiori in cobalt blue, pale pink, pale green, and white about a central cane with two dancing figures, the inner ring with twelve dog canes, the next-to-outer ring with four dog canes. Signed "SL" in fourth ring.
Diam. 3 1/8″ (7.9 cm.)

PLATE 9

1965.387.C *(top)* France, Clichy, c. 1845–50.
Spaced concentric of three rings of canes in blues, pinks, greens, and white about a center of red canes set in a translucent cranberry ground.
Diam. 3 3/16" (8.1 cm.)

1965.339.C *(bottom)* France, Clichy, c. 1845–50.
Miniature spaced concentric of two rings, the inner blue, the outer with lavender-sheathed roses set into a turkey-red ground.
Diam. 1 7/8" (4.7 cm.)

PLATE 10

1965.335.C *(top)* France, Clichy, c. 1845–50.
Spaced concentric of three rings of canes in pink, white, and green on a deep cobalt blue over white ground. Reground. Flat base.
Diam. 2 3/16" (5.5 cm.)

1965.217.C *(top right)* France, Clichy, c. 1845–50.
Spaced concentric of two rings of canes in pale pinks and greens on a deep cobalt blue ground.
Diam. 2 3/16" (5.5 cm.)

1965.88.C *(left)* France, Clichy, c. 1845–50.
Concentric of three rings of canes predominately in lilac, pea green, and white set into a rich pink over white ground.
Diam. 3 1/8" (7.9 cm.)

1965.114.C *(bottom right)* France, Clichy, c. 1845–50.
Concentric of three rows of canes, the outer in red and white, the others predominately pale green, pale pink, and white set into a rich blue-violet over white ground, which they indent. Base reground flat.
Diam. 3 1/8" (7.9 cm.)

1965.238.C *(bottom)* France, Clichy, c. 1845–50.
Spaced concentric of three rings of canes in pink, apple green, and white about a central green cane, all set in a deep cobalt blue ground.
Diam. 2 5/8" (6.7 cm.)

PLATE 11

1965.410.C *(top)* France, Clichy, c. 1845–50.
Concentric with two rows of red, white, pink, and blue canes, including a rose, about a central red cane, all set into an apple green ground.
Diam. 2 7/16" (6.2 cm.)

1939.95.C *(left)* France, Clichy, c. 1845–50.
Miniature concentric with two rings of green, pink, and white canes about a central pink cane, all set on a deep opaque ultramarine ground.
Diam. 1 13/16" (4.6 cm.)

1965.272.C *(right)* France, Clichy, c. 1845–50.
Miniature spaced concentric with two rows of pink and white canes about a deep maroon cane, all set on a brilliant cerulean blue ground.
Diam. 1 3/4" (4.4 cm.)

1965.55.C *(center)* France, Clichy, c. 1845–50.
Concentric with two rings of white and green canes about a central aqua blue cane, all set into a pink over white ground. Reground.
Diam. 2 9/16" (6.5 cm.)

1965.115.C *(bottom)* France, Clichy, c. 1845–50.
Spaced concentric with two rings of aqua blue, white, and green canes set on a brilliant scarlet over white ground. Reground.
Diam. 2 3/8″ (6 cm.)

PLATE 12

1965.414.C *(top left)* France, Clichy, c. 1845–50.
Hexagonal panel of canes in pinks, pale blue, and green, with prototype roses at the panel edges, all set flush with a deep ultramarine over white ground. Center cane signed "C."
Diam. 3″ (7.6 cm.)

1965.275.C *(top right)* France, Clichy, c. 1845–50.
Hexagonal panel of canes in pink, white, blue, and purple set flush with an apple green over white ground. Reground.
Diam. 3 1/8″ (7.9 cm.)

1965.211.SL *(center)* France, Saint-Louis, c. 1845–50.
Jasper ground divided by white spokes into eight pie-shaped panels of alternately blue and white and red and white jasper, each panel with a single cane in blue or pink about a central figure cane representing Punch. Spiral red and white torsade not visible from top. Reground.
Diam. 2 7/8″ (7.3 cm.)

1965.411.C *(bottom left)* France, Clichy, c. 1845–50.
Eight panels of canes, each panel containing canes all of one type, and two pale green and lilac rings about a central white cane, all set flush with a pale pink over white ground.
Diam. 3 1/8″ (7.9 cm.)

1965.308.C *(bottom right)* France, Clichy, c. 1845–50.
Six crossing spokes of canes about a central aqua cane set flush into a white ground. Rare design. Reground.
Diam. 2 7/8″ (7.3 cm.)

PLATE 13

1965.463.SL France, Saint-Louis, c. 1845–50.
Four close millefiori panels divided by a cross of white canes bordered by pale pistachio spiral ribbon. Central blue cane.
Diam. 2 13/16″ (7.1 cm.)

PLATE 14

1965.471.C France, Clichy, c. 1845–50.
Intertwined garlands of white and wine red canes and two circles of pink and purple canes about a white central cane, all set in a carpet ground of grass canes punctuated with tiny white star rods. Rare. Some careful regrinding.
Diam. 3 3/16″ (8.1 cm.)

PLATE 15

1965.431.C *(top)* France, Clichy, c. 1845–50.
Five C-scrolls of canes, each scroll a different color, about a circle of roses enclosing a green cane, in clear glass, the top with a circular punty, the sides precisely cut in long concave hexagons.
Diam. 2 11/16″ (6.8 cm.)

1965.445.C *(left)* France, Clichy, c. 1845–50.
Two intertwined garlands in pink and green with two inner rings of canes in pale aqua and wine red about a central green and red cane, all on an upset muslin ground with long parallel filigree rods beneath it, the weight cut with alternating circular punties and vertical flutes. Diam. 3 3/16″ (8.1 cm.)

1965.443.C *(right)* France, Clichy, 1845–50.
Cologne or scent bottle, the base set with five C-scrolls of canes, each scroll a different color, about a central ring of amethyst canes enclosing a rose, all on an upset muslin ground with parallel filigree rods beneath, the bottle with straight, faceted baluster neck, the sides cut with raised oval punties alternating with long vertical flutes. Stopper shows two rings of canes in lettuce green and amethyst about a rose, all on upset muslin ground; stopper is similarly cut. Overall height 6 5/8″ (16.8 cm.); diam. of bottle 3 3/8″ (8.6 cm.)

1965.393.C *(bottom)* France, Clichy, c. 1845–50.
Star weight, the star composed of three garlands of bright aqua, red, and green grass canes about a central rose, all on an upset muslin ground, the underside with parallel filigree rods. Diam. 3 1/8″ (7.9 cm.)

PLATE 16

1965.106.SL *(top left)* France, Saint-Louis, c. 1845–50.
Six alternating white and blue and yellow looped garlands about a blue and yellow center cane set in a deep salmon over white ground, indenting it, the top cut in a flat hexagon, the sides with six flat panels. Reground.
Diam. 3″ (7.6 cm.)

1965.416.C *(top right)* France, Clichy, c. 1845–50.
Garland of six touching circles of canes, each circle a different color, about a central red cane within a circle of green canes, all set in a cerulean blue over white ground, which they indent. Diam. 2 7/8″ (7.3 cm.)

1965.90.SL *(center left)* France, Saint-Louis, c. 1845–50.
Marbrie of four cerulean blue and white festoons about a central cane cluster in pink, lettuce green, and white.
Diam. 3 1/8″ (7.9 cm.)

1965.80.SL *(center right)* France, Saint-Louis, c. 1845–50.
Six alternate red and white and pink and blue looped garlands of canes about a central white cane set flush in a citron yellow over white ground. Reground.
Diam. 3″ (7.6 cm.)

1965.65.C *(bottom left)* France, Clichy, c. 1845–50.
Pentafoil of pale pink and green canes with a central green circle about a white cane, all set in a deep amethyst over white ground.
Diam. 2 11/16″ (6.8 cm.)

1965.314.SL *(bottom right)* France, Saint-Louis, c. 1845–50.
Marbrie in four cerulean blue and white festoons, a central cane cluster in pink, lettuce green, and white. Perhaps made as a pair with the one at center left.
Diam. 3 1/8″ (7.9 cm.)

PLATE 17

1965.399.SL *(top)* France, Saint-Louis, c. 1845–50.
Carpet ground of green-lined white crimped canes, the ground inset with five circles of pale pink canes about five figure canes, including a dog, horse, camel, dancing girl, and running devil; with a central cane cluster in white and blue.
Diam. 2 3/8″ (6 cm.)

1965.429.SL *(center)* France, Saint-Louis, c. 1845–50.
Carpet ground of red-lined aqua blue and white cog canes, the ground inset with five clusters of white canes about green and white canes, the central group of mauve, green, and white containing a Punch silhouette.
Diam. 2 5/8″ (6.7 cm.)

1965.190.B *(bottom)* France, Baccarat, 1848.
Carpet ground of green-white-red star canes inset with spaced millefiori canes, including animal silhouettes and one cane dated "B. 1848." Filigree stuffing inside cushion.
Diam. 3 1/8″ (7.9 cm.)

PLATE 18

1965.216.SL France, Saint-Louis, c. 1845–50.
Tricolor carpet ground, the two concentric bands of coral and white canes about a blue cluster. Reground.
Diam. 2 3/4″ (7 cm.)

PLATE 19

1965.340.C *(top center)* France, Clichy, c. 1845–50.
Doorknob with close millefiori canes including one pink and two white roses, all in a white and cobalt blue stave basket, the knob undercut with flat facets and mounted in a brass fitting.
Overall length 2″ (5.1 cm.); diam. 1 5/8″ (4.2 cm.)

1965.222.B *(top right)* France, Baccarat, c. 1845–50.
Close millefiori mushroom with torsade consisting of a white filigree cable encircled by a counterclockwise cobalt blue spiral. Star-cut base. Reground.
Diam. 2 3/4″ (7 cm.)

1965.59.B *(center)* France, Baccarat, c. 1845–50.
Close millefiori mushroom with torsade consisting of a white gauze cable encircled by a counterclockwise cobalt blue spiral, the sides of the weight cut with oval punties. No top punty. Star-cut base.
Diam. 2 3/4″ (7 cm.)

1965.285.C *(bottom right)* France, Clichy, c. 1845–50.
Close millefiori doorknob, the tightly packed canes including eight roses, in a basket of pink and white staves, the sides undercut with flat facets. Unmounted.
Overall length 1 5/8″ (4.2 cm.); diam. 1 3/4″ (4.4 cm.)

1965.103.C *(bottom center)* France, Clichy, c. 1845–50.
Close millefiori mushroom, the canes including a mauve rose all in a pink and white stave basket, the top table cut, the sides cut with five large circular punties. Base petal cut.
Diam. 3 3/16″ (8.1 cm.)

1965.113.C *(far left)* France, Clichy, c. 1845–50.
Close millefiori mushroom, the canes including six roses, all set in a blue and white stave basket, the top table cut, the sides cut with five large circular punties. Base petal cut. Frosted rim.
Diam. 3 1/8″ (7.9 cm.)

PLATE 20

1965.187.SL *(top left)* France, Saint-Louis, c. 1845–50.
Concentric millefiori mushroom, the canes in rings of pink, green, and white about a central blue and green cane, the torsade a cobalt blue coil clockwise about a white chaplet bead twist. Base star cut.
Diam. 2 15/16″ (7.4 cm.)

1965.284.SL *(top right)* France, Saint-Louis, c. 1845–50.
Concentric millefiori mushroom with four rings of pistachio green, coral, cobalt blue, and white canes about a red-white-blue center cane, the sides cut with twenty-eight graduated circular punties and one on top. No torsade.
Diam. 2 7/8″ (7.3 cm.)

1965.388.B *(center)* France, Baccarat, c. 1845–50.
Concentric millefiori mushroom with four rings of canes in pink white, red green, red-centered white, and blue arrow canes about a shamrock central cane, the torsade with counterclockwise cobalt blue spiral about a gauze cable. Star-cut base. Rough rim.
Diam. 2 3/4″ (7 cm.)

1965.224.B *(bottom left)* France, Baccarat, c. 1845–50.
Concentric millefiori mushroom with four rings of white, pink, and green canes about a central arrow cane, the inner ring also with arrow canes. Torsade has counterclockwise cobalt blue spiral about a white chaplet bead twist. Star-cut base.
Diam. 2 3/8″ (7.9 cm.)

1965.109.SL *(bottom right)* France, Saint-Louis, c. 1845–50.
Concentric millefiori mushroom with seven rings of canes in various colors about a center cane of pink crimped rods, the torsade with a cobalt blue clockwise spiral about a chaplet bead twist. Star-cut base.
Diam. 3″ (7.6 cm.)

PLATE 21

1965.476.C *(top left)* France, Clichy, c. 1845–50.
Concentric millefiori mushroom with four rings of close-packed canes, the inner ring of Clichy roses, the outer of green grass canes, all sheathed in white and cadmium green staves, the weight cut with one top and six side punties. Flat base is star cut.
Diam. 2 3/4″ (7 cm.)

1965.163.C *(top right)* France, Clichy, c. 1845–50.
Concentric millefiori mushroom with five rings of canes, the next-to-inner with six Clichy roses alternating with six green canes, all sheathed in white staves, the weight cut with one top and five side punties. Base petal cut.
Diam. 2 3/4″ (7 cm.)

1965.184.B *(center)* France, Baccarat, c. 1845–50.
Concentric millefiori mushroom with four rings of canes, the inner white sheathed in wine red with red quatrefoil center rods, the outer purple with pink centers and hidden beneath the mushroom rim. Torsade with cobalt blue counterclockwise spiral about a gauze cable. Base star cut.
Diam. 3 1/8″ (7.9 cm.)

1965.57.B *(bottom left)* France, Baccarat, c. 1845–50.
Rare concentric millefiori mushroom with four rings of canes about a central ruffled cane, the next-to-outer ring with eleven Clichy-like roses in smoked salmon and pink, the mushroom sheathed in white staves. Well-placed torsade of counterclockwise cobalt spiral about a gauze cable. Top table cut, the sides with five panels. Base star cut.
Diam. 2 7/8″ (7.3 cm.)

1965.107.C *(bottom right)* France, Clichy, c. 1845–50.
Concentric millefiori mushroom with four rings of canes about a pink Clichy rose, the inner ring with eleven rare green roses, the next with seven white roses, the design sheathed in white and pink staves, the top table cut, the sides with six circular punties. Flat base star cut.
Diam. 2 3/4″ (7 cm.)

PLATE 22

1965.214.SL *(top)* France, Saint-Louis, c. 1845–50.
Small concentric millefiori mushroom of four rings of canes about a green and red center cane, the outer ring white with blue star centers, the weight cut with one top and six circular side punties. Amber-flashed base.
Diam. 2 13/16″ (7.1 cm.)

1965.210.SL *(bottom)* France, Saint-Louis, c. 1845–50.
Concentric millefiori mushroom with six rings of canes predominantly in blue, white, and amber, with a coral pink clockwise spiral about a white chaplet bead twist. Base star cut.
Diam. 2 3/4″ (7 cm.)

PLATE 23

1965.189.B *(center left)* France, Baccarat, c. 1845–50.
Cobalt blue over white double overlay cut with one top and six circular side punties, the motif a close millefiori mushroom. Star-cut base.
Diam. 3″ (7.6 cm.)

1965.284.C *(top right)* France, Clichy, c. 1845–50.
"Turquoise" over white double overlay with five side punties, the top table cut, the motif a concentric millefiori mushroom with five rings of canes in red, green, blue, and pink, all sheathed in white staves. Frosted, slightly concave base lightly crosshatched.
Diam. 2 11/16″ (6.8 cm.)

1965.160.C *(bottom left)* France, Clichy, c. 1845–50.
"Turquoise" over white double overlay with five side punties, table-cut top, the motif a close millefiori mushroom with seven roses, all sheathed in white staves. Slightly concave base crosshatched.
Diam. 2 11/16″ (6.8 cm.)

1965.94.C *(center right)* France, Clichy, c. 1845–50.
"Turquoise" over white double overlay cut with five side punties, table-cut top, the motif a concentric millefiori mushroom of four rows in mauve, pink, and green, the inner row of ten pink roses, all sheathed in a white stave basket. Slightly concave base crosshatched.
Diam. 2 3/4″ (7 cm.)

PLATE 24

1965.481.C *(top)* France, Clichy, c. 1845–50.
Opalescent white overlay cut with five side punties, table-cut top, the motif a concentric millefiori mushroom with six rings of canes in pink, mauve, ruby, white, and green about a central pink rose, the fourth ring with eleven white roses, the whole sheathed in white and pink staves. Nearly flat base, crosshatched.
Diam. 3 1/16″ (7.8 cm.)

1965.492.SL *(center)* France, Saint-Louis, c. 1845–50.
Concentric millefiori mushroom with six rows of white, amber, coral, and blue canes, with a clockwise pink spiral about a chaplet bead torsade. Unusual faceting with the top halves of the six side punties cut away, leaving a star-shaped flat top. Base star cut. Undoubtedly reground.
Diam. 3″ (7.6 cm.)

1965.367.SL *(bottom)* France, Saint-Louis, c. 1845–50.
Small concentric millefiori mushroom with three rings of canes in white, coral, and coral-centered aquamarine canes about a central blue and chartreuse green cog cane, the octagonal top and sides cut with petal cuts and circular punties.
Diam. 2 7/16″ (6.2 cm.)

PLATE 25

1965.95.BS *(top left)* England, Bacchus, c. 1845–50.
Magnum concentric millefiori mushroom with six rings of red, white, and blue canes, four of the rows ruffled canes, the outer row red-lined crimped canes, the large motif surrounded by a clockwise opaque blue spiral about a white chaplet bead twist, the torsade set well up off the base. Base has wide, flat rim.
Diam. 3 5/8″ (9.3 cm.)

1965.475.BS *(right)* England, Bacchus, c. 1845–50.
Rare concentric millefiori tuft of pink, pale acid green, pale lemon, and dead ink blue canes, all in a pink and white double overlay basket with handle, the basket further encased in clear glass. Millefiori design shows in miniature beneath pontil mark. Magnum.
Diam. 3 3/8″ (8.6 cm.)

1965.268.BS *(bottom left)* England, Bacchus, c. 1845–50.
Magnum concentric millefiori mushroom with four rings of blue, pink, white, and pale emerald green canes about a central pink ruffled cane, all framed in a clockwise opaque blue spiral about a white chaplet bead twist. Base has wide, flat rim, showing considerable wear.
Diam. 3 7/8″ (9.9 cm.)

PLATE 26

1965.183.C *(top left)* France, Clichy, c. 1845–50.
Pedestal weight with concentric design of eight tightly packed rows of canes, in soft greens, pink, lilac, one ring with fourteen white roses, all about a central pink rose and sheathed in white and apple green staves. Footed base. Weight badly cracked below girdle.
Diam. 2 15/16″ (7.4 cm.)

1965.385.C *(top right)* France, Clichy, c. 1845–50.
Pedestal weight with concentric design of five rings of canes, the third in aquamarine blue, all about four red scalloped canes and sheathed in white and royal blue staves. Footed base is flat.
Diam. 2 7/8″ (7.3 cm.)

1965.86.SL *(center)* France, Saint-Louis, c. 1845–50.
Pedestal weight with close millefiori design divided into four panels by a cross of green-centered white canes, the foot at the base a filigree cable and undercut beneath to reveal a band of latticinio.
Diam. 3 1/16″ (7.8 cm.)

1965.195.C *(far left)* France, Clichy, c. 1845–50.
Miniature pedestal with a superbly packed concentric millefiori design of five rings of canes in pink, green, purple and white, ruby, and grass green, all about a central white rose and sheathed in white and pink staves. Footed base.
Diam. 1 7/8″ (4.7 cm.)

1965.158.C *(bottom left)* France, Clichy, c. 1845–50.
Pedestal with exquisite concentric millefiori design of four rings of green, wine red, mauve, and pink canes, the next-to-outer row with eight pale pink roses, all sheathed in white and pink staves. Flat, footed base frosted on edge and attacked with sharp instrument.
Diam. 2 1/8″ (5.4 cm.)

1965.157.C *(bottom right)* France, Clichy, c. 1845–50.
Pedestal with concentric millefiori design of five rings of canes predominantly in white, red, and green, about five central purple canes, all sheathed in white and amethyst staves. Footed base.
Diam. 2 3/4″ (7 cm.)

PLATE 27

1965.456.SL France, Saint-Louis, 1848.
Concentric pedestal, the tightly packed, neatly arranged rows in pastel tints, including chartreuse yellow, above an elaborate filigree cabled foot, one deep purple cane in the outer row signed and dated "SL.1848."
Diam. 3 1/8" (7.9 cm.)

PLATE 28

1965.86.SL France, Saint-Louis, c. 1845–50.
Same weight as seen upright in center of Plate 26.

PLATE 29

1965.408.C *(top left)* France, Clichy, c. 1845–50.
Swirl weight, the apple green and white swirls radiating from a central cane in white and red, enclosed in a cobalt ruffle.
Diam. 2 5/16" (5.9 cm.)

1965.390.C *(center)* France, Clichy, c. 1845–50.
Spoke weight with spaced white, amethyst, and forest green rods radiating from a central red whorl and white star cane, clear glass visible between the rods. Rare.
Diam. 3 1/4" (8.3 cm.)

1965.355.C *(top right)* France, Clichy, c. 1845–50.
Swirl weight, the lilac and white swirls radiating almost like spokes from a central green and white cane. Reground.
Diam. 2 1/16" (5.2 cm.)

1965.428.BO *(bottom left)* Bohemia, c. 1845–50.
Swirl weight with seven canes, including a Clichy-like rose and a dog silhouette, all over a swirl of white and pink rods. Rare.
Diam. 2 5/16" (5.9 cm.)

1965.194.BO *(center right)* Bohemia, c. 1845–50.
Spoke weight with spaced white and cobalt-blue spokes radiating from central red cane and topped by a circle of five canes, including two dog silhouettes. Rare.
Diam. 2 5/8" (6.7 cm.)

1965.348.C *(bottom)* France, Clichy, c. 1845–50.
Miniature swirl weight with tightly knit pink and white swirls about a central green and red cane.
Diam. 1 13/16" (4.6 cm.)

1965.318.C *(bottom right)* France, Clichy, c. 1845–50.
Swirl weight with tightly knit apple green and white swirls radiating from a blue-green-red cane. Reground.
Diam. 2 1/16" (5.2 cm.)

PLATE 30

1965.142.C *(top left)* France, Clichy, c. 1845–50.
Swirl weight of white and medium cobalt blue rods well knit and radiating from a large pink and white ruffled cane. Reground.
Diam. 3 1/16" (7.8 cm.)

1965.421.C *(top)* France, Clichy, c. 1845–50.
Swirl weight of white, pink, and lettuce green rods radiating from a large red-centered white and green cane. Color combination rare.
Diam. 3 1/8″ (7.9 cm.)

1965.474.C *(top right)* France, Clichy, c. 1845–50.
Swirl weight of white and amethyst rods radiating from a red-centered green and white ruffled cane.
Diam. 3 3/16″ (8.1 cm.)

1965.369.C *(center)* France, Clichy, c. 1845–50.
Swirl weight of spaced white, "turquoise" blue, and pale pink rods radiating from a pale pink and white cane. Some bubbles.
Diam. 3 1/8″ (7.9 cm.)

1965.334.C *(bottom left)* France, Clichy, c. 1845–50.
Swirl weight with white and "turquoise" blue rods radiating from a white-green-red cane. Reground.
Diam. 2 1/2″ (6.3 cm.)

1965.317.C *(bottom right)* France, Clichy, c. 1845–50.
Swirl weight with tightly knit white and pink rods radiating from a green and white Clichy rose. Reground.
Diam. 2 5/8″ (6.7 cm.)

PLATE 31

1965.93.SL (A) *(top left)* France, Saint-Louis, c. 1845–50.
Hollow-blown crown paperweight shot cup, the paperweight of alternating filigree twists and spiral red and green over white ribbons, yellow center cane, surmounted by a bell-shaped bowl with pink and white twist rim.
Height 3 3/4″ (9.6 cm.); paperweight diam. 2 1/8″ (5.4 cm.)

1965.93.SL (B) *(top right)* France, Saint-Louis, c. 1845–50.
Hollow-blown crown shot cup, the paperweight of alternating filigree twists and spiral red and green over white ribbons, blue center cane, surmounted by a bell-shaped bowl with blue and white twist rim.
Height 3 5/8″ (9.3 cm.); paperweight diam. 2 1/8″ (5.4 cm.)

1965.444.SL *(center bottom)* France, Saint-Louis, c. 1845–50.
Hollow-blown crown paperweight of alternating filigree twists and aventurine-flecked amber over white twisted ribbons, centered by a large blue and white cane, the base drilled with a hole. Collection of King Farouk.
Diam. 3 1/4″ (8.3 cm.)

PLATE 32

1965.301.SL (A) (B) *(top left and right)* France, Saint-Louis, c. 1845–50.
Hollow-blown crown paperweight shot cups, the weights with red and green over white twisted ribbons, alternating with filigree twists, the design swirled from a central cane with a white star on blue in the Clichy manner, the cup with a spiral decoration of white rods. A pair, the one at right slightly shorter.
Height 3 7/8″ (9.9 cm.)

1965.370.SL *(center)* France, Saint-Louis, c. 1845–50.
Hollow-blown crown paperweight vase or shot cup, the weight with blue and red over white twisted ribbons alternating with filigree twists radiating from a central cane, the vessel overlaid in translucent cobalt blue and cut with seven flat vertical panels, the rim with a clockwise filigree twist. Brass cap joins vessel to weight. Bottom drilled.
Height 5 1/4″ (13.3 cm.)

1965.436.SL *(bottom left)* France, Saint-Louis, c. 1845–50.
Hollow-blown crown weight with rich green and red over white twisted ribbons alternating with filigree twists radiating from a central blue and white cane.
Diam. 2 11/16″ (6.8 cm.)

1965.197.SL *(bottom right)* France, Saint-Louis, c. 1845–50.
Miniature hollow-blown crown weight with red and green over white twist ribbons alternating with filigree twists radiating from a central red and white cane with green whorl center.
Diam. 1 11/16″ (4.3 cm.)

PLATE 33

1965.376.SL *(top left)* France, Saint-Louis, 1845.
Hollow-blown egg-shaped hand cooler with scrambled canes and filigree close to the surface.
Dated "S.L. 1845."
Length 2 1/2″ (6.3 cm.)

1965.173.B *(top)* France, Baccarat, c. 1845–50.
Hollow-blown egg-shaped hand cooler, the pink over white double overlay cut with graduated punties, one end star cut.
Length 2 3/4″ (7 cm.)

1965.174.B *(top right)* France, Baccarat, c. 1845–50.
Hollow-blown egg-shaped hand cooler, the forest green over white double overlay cut with graduated punties, one end star cut.
Length 2 5/8″ (6.7 cm.)

1965.172.SL *(bottom left)* France, Saint-Louis, c. 1845–50.
Hollow-blown egg-shaped hand cooler, the Dubarry pink over white double overlay cut in panels in which punties alternate with vines and berries.
Length 2 3/8″ (6 cm.)

1965.171.SL *(bottom right)* France, Saint-Louis, c. 1845–50.
Hollow-blown egg-shaped hand cooler, the double overlay cut in panels alternately of white, and blue over white, both showing graduated punties.
Length 2 11/16″ (6.8 cm.)

PLATE 34

1965.229.B *(top left)* France, Baccarat, c. 1845–50.
Pansy of the usual type, with two upper deep purple petals and three lower yellow petals spotted with purple, ten light emerald green leaves, and bud, the dome on one side engraved with the monogram "JWF."
Diam. 2 15/16″ (7.4 cm.)

1965.490.SL *(top right)* France, Saint-Louis, c. 1845–50.
Pansy with two upper mauve and three lower purple-bordered amber petals, sulphur yellow center, four green leaves, and curved stem. Base star cut.
Diam. 2 9/16″ (6.5 cm.)

1965.266.B. *(center)* France, Baccarat, c. 1845–50.
Pansy of rare type, with two very deep purple upper petals, the lower three petals of translucent yellow bordered with deep purple, eight leaves, and bud, all over an upset muslin ground with a ring of red-white-green alternating with turquoise and white canes, the dome cut with six large flat facets. Red, blue, green filigree stuffing under ground.
Diam. 3 1/4″ (8.3 cm.)

1965.193.C *(bottom left)* France, Clichy, c. 1845–50.
Pansy or viola with mauve and cream-colored petals striped in mauve, with two stems, five leaves of varying shades of green, and bud, all over a delicate latticinio ground. Reground.
Diam. 2 7/8″ (7.3 cm.)

1965.78.B *(bottom center)* France, Baccarat, c. 1845–50.
Pansy with one upper purple and the other upper plum-colored petal, the lower three petals of cobalt blue with white crow's-feet and white cogged edge, with five leaves and bud, the weight cut with six circular side punties and one top punty. Star-cut base.
Diam. 2 1/2″ (6.3 cm.)

1965.289.C *(bottom right)* France, Clichy, c. 1845–50.
Viola with two deep lilac upper and three cream lower petals, with two green leaves and bud. Reground.
Diam. 1. 15/16″ (4.9 cm.)

PLATE 35

1965.401.B *(top left)* France, Baccarat, c. 1845–50.
Pale yellow clematis with red whorl, white-starred center cane, petals showing clear glass between the veins, with eight green leaves and yellow bud. One petal cracked. Star-cut base.
Diam. 2 13/16″ (7.1 cm.)

1965.261.SL *(top right)* France, Saint-Louis, c. 1845–50.
Large white clematis, the petals striped with pink, and a smaller pink clematis with yellow center, seven green leaves, and two intertwined stems.
Diam. 2 5/8″ (6.7 cm.)

1965.273.SL *(center)* France, Saint-Louis, c. 1845–50.
Bright cobalt blue clematis with red and yellow center and five green leaves (one cracked) over an amber-flashed base, the weight cut with one top and five side circular punties.
Diam. 3 1/8″ (7.9 cm.)

1965.395.SL *(bottom left)* France, Saint-Louis, c. 1845–50.
Large cobalt blue clematis with amber cog center and four green leaves. Star-cut base.
Diam. 3 1/16″ (7.8 cm.)

1965.123.SL *(bottom right)* France, Saint-Louis, c. 1845–50.
A red and white clematis, both with sulphur yellow centers, and four green leaves and stems, all set flush in a brilliant cobalt blue over white ground. Reground.
Diam. 2 5 /8″ (6.7 cm.)

PLATE 36

1965.127.B *(top left)* France, Baccarat, c. 1845–50.
White clematis with arrow-cane center and eight green leaves and bud, all within a circle of alternately red and white ruffled canes. Star-cut base.
Diam. 3 1/8″ (7.9 cm.)

1965.397.SL *(top right)* France, Saint-Louis, c. 1845–50.
White clematis with mottled yellow and red center and four variable green leaves and stem, on fine green and white jasper ground. Sides cut with seven circular punties, top table cut.
Diam. 2 1/2″ (6.3 cm.)

1965.461.SL *(center)* France, Saint-Louis, c. 1845–50.
Translucent white clematis with blue and amber cog center, with five chartreuse leaves, set on a deep lustrous green aventurine over white ground, the ground indented by a coral pink clockwise cable torsade about a white chaplet beaded twist.
Diam. 3″ (7.6 cm.)

1965.76.SL *(bottom left)* France, Saint-Louis, c. 1845–50.
A white clematis with a center of three pink seeds on sulphur yellow, the flower with three green leaves and stem set flush in a lustrous green aventurine ground, the ground indented by a clockwise torsade of red and white spiral thread.
Diam. 3 1/4″ (8.3 cm.)

1965.168.SL *(bottom right)* France, Saint-Louis, c. 1845–50.
White clematis with mottled yellow and brown center and four light green leaves and stem set on a red and white jasper ground.
Diam. 3″ (7.6 cm.)

PLATE 37

1965.234.B *(top left)* France, Baccarat, c. 1845–50.
Pale blue clematis with red whorl, white-starred center cane and five upper and two long lower leaves, the weight recut with flat gem facets. Star-cut base.
Diam. 2 3/8″ (6 cm.)

1965.239.B *(top right)* France, Baccarat, c. 1845–50.
Brilliant vermilion primrose neatly banded in white with a red whorl, white-starred center cane and eleven rich emerald leaves in three groups with stems, the weight cut with one top and six circular side punties. Star-cut base.
Diam. 2 15/16″ (7.4 cm.)

1965.228.B *(center left)* France, Baccarat, c. 1845–50.
White clematis with red whorl, white-starred center cane and three emerald upper and two lower leaves, the intertwined stems terminating in white buds. Cut with six circular side punties and one top punty. Star-cut base.
Diam. 2 1/8″ (5.4 cm.)

1965.202.B *(center right)* France, Baccarat, c. 1845–50.
Red primrose banded in white with a center pale yellow honeycomb cane, with eight green leaves and red bud, all within a circle of alternating white and green canes. Star-cut base.
Diam. 3 1/8″ (7.9 cm.)

1965.116.B *(bottom left)* France, Baccarat, c. 1845–50.
Deep pink clematis with red whorl, white-starred center and five emerald leaves, the intertwined stem terminating in pink buds. Star-cut base.
Diam. 2 3/16″ (5.6 cm.)

1965.417.B *(bottom right)* France, Baccarat, c. 1845–50.
Pink anemone, the ogee petals edged in white, with red whorl, white-starred center together with eleven green leaves in four groups; the weight cut with one top and six circular side punties. Star-cut base.
Diam. 3 1/4″ (8.3 cm.)

PLATE 38

1965.238.B *(far left)* France, Baccarat, c. 1845–50.
Primrose with five deep cobalt blue ogee petals bordered in white with white star and red whorl center and eleven green leaves in three groups, the weight cut with one top and six circular side punties. Star-cut base.
Diam. 2 7/8″ (7.3 cm.)

1965.287.B *(top center)* France, Baccarat, c. 1845–50.
Primrose with five pink ogee petals edged in white, the usual white-starred, red whorl center cane, and eleven green leaves and stems in three groups, the sides recut with twenty-two vertical flutes.
Diam. 2 3/4″ (7 cm.)

1965.121.B *(top right)* France, Baccarat, c. 1845–50.
Primrose with five cobalt blue ogee petals bordered in white, the usual white-starred, red whorl center cane, and three upper and two long lower leaves and stem. Base star cut.
Diam. 2 1/8″ (5.4 cm.)

1965.291.B *(right center)* France, Baccarat, c. 1845–50.
Anemone with six ribbed white petals edged in blue, the usual red whorl, white-starred center cane, and ten green leaves and stems in three groups, the weight cut with one top and six circular side punties. Star-cut base.
Diam. 3 1/8″ (7.9 cm.)

1965.245.B *(bottom center)* France, Baccarat, c. 1845–50.
Anemone with six ribbed white petals edged in red, the usual red whorl and white-starred center cane, and eleven green leaves and stems in three groups. Star-cut base. Reground.
Diam. 3 1/8″ (7.9 cm.)

PLATE 39

1965.240.B *(top)* France, Baccarat, c. 1845–50.
Five closed clematis buds in pink and white on tall and entwined stems, as if espaliered, with two upper and two long lower leaves, the weight gem recut with flat pentagons, the top and star-cut base a flat hexagon.
Diam. 2 3/16″ (5.6 cm.)

1965.101.B *(center)* France, Baccarat, c. 1845–50.
Six closed pink clematis buds espaliered on long intertwined stems with four upper and two long lower green leaves, the weight gem-recut with graduated flat pentagons in three tiers. Star-cut base.
Diam. 3 3/16″ (8.1 cm.)

1965.63.B *(bottom)* France, Baccarat, c. 1845–50.
Five closed pale aqua clematis buds on intertwined stems with two upper and two long lower green leaves. Star-cut base.
Diam. 2 3/4″ (7 cm.)

PLATE 40

1965.363.SL *(top left)* France, Saint-Louis, c. 1845–50.
Aster with long cobalt blue petals, Naples yellow center cane, and five green leaves and stem set over a latticinio ground. Minimally reground.
Diam. 2 3/4″ (7 cm.)

1965.288.SL *(top right)* France, Saint-Louis, c. 1845–50.
Dahlia-related flower with two layers of brilliant red petals, a sulphur yellow coiled center, and five deep green leaves and stem, all placed above a bold latticinio ground.
Diam. 2 11/16″ (6.8 cm.)

1965.67.SL *(center left)* France, Saint-Louis, c. 1845–50.
Large purple dahlia of many veined petals with star and amber center cane, five spaced green leaves. Flat star-cut base. Reground. One petal cracked.
Diam. 3 1/4″ (8.3 cm.)

1965.122.SL *(center right)* France, Saint-Louis, c. 1845–50.
Pink many-petaled dahlia with star and green center cane and five spaced green leaves. Flat star-cut base.
Diam. 2 5/8″ (6.7 cm.)

1965.278.SL *(bottom left)* France, Saint-Louis, c. 1845–50.
Uncommon dahlia, the amber petals striped with brown about a tiny blue cog center cane and five spaced green leaves. Base cut with a deep concave star.
Diam. 2 1/2″ (6.3 cm.)

1965.470.SL *(bottom right)* France, Saint-Louis, c. 1845–50.
Brilliant deep pink dahlia with sulphur-spotted center and nine green leaves and stem.
Reground.
Diam. 3 1/4″ (8.3 cm.)

PLATE 41

1965.56.SL *(top left)* France, Saint-Louis, c. 1845–50.
Feathery white pom-pom with lemon yellow and coral center cane and four green leaves and
stem, with a white bud, set over a warm pink latticinio ground.
Diam. 2 15/16″ (7.4 cm.)

1965.446.B *(top right)* France, Baccarat, c. 1845–50.
Peach-colored pom-pom with pale yellow center, two fine long coral and green buds, and
seven green leaves and stem, the flower encircled by a ring of alternately blue and red canes.
Cut around sides with six oval punties. Low dome. Star-cut base.
Diam. 2 3/8″ (6 cm.)

1965.230.SL *(center left)* France, Saint-Louis, c. 1845–50.
Cool pink pom-pom with blue and chartreuse yellow center cane, warm pink bud, four green
leaves and stem set over a white latticinio ground. Flat base. Reground.
Diam. 2 11/16″ (6.8 cm.)

1965.71.B *(center right)* French, Baccarat, c. 1845–50(?).
Brilliant white pom-pom with yellow center, white bud, and eight green leaves and stem, set
within a ring of alternating red and blue arrow canes. Star-cut base.
Diam. 3″ (7.6 cm.)

1965.68.SL *(bottom left)* France, Saint-Louis, c. 1845–50.
White pom-pom with yellow center, white bud, and four green leaves and stem set over a
tomato-colored ground. Carefully reground.
Diam. 2 3/4″ (7 cm.)

1965.96.B *(bottom right)* France, Baccarat, c. 1845–50.
Pale copper-colored pom-pom with yellow center, two long coral and green buds, and seven
green leaves and stem, all within a ring of alternating green canes and red-centered white
canes. Star-cut base. Reground.
Diam. 2 13/16″ (7.1 cm.)

PLATE 42

1965.143.B *(top left)* France, Baccarat, c. 1845–50.
Flower with six pale yellow petals touched with burnt sienna, with a white star and red whorl
center cane, a yellow bud, and nine light green leaves and stem. Star-cut base.
Diam. 3 1/8″ (7.9 cm.)

1965.306.B *(top right)* France, Baccarat, c. 1845–50.
A flower with five spaced tomato red petals about a green whorl, white-starred center cane,
with tomato red bud and eight green leaves and stem, the weight cut with one top and six
circular side punties. Star-cut base.
Diam. 2 7/8″ (7.3 cm.)

1965.72.SL *(bottom left)* France, Saint-Louis, c. 1845–50.
Brilliant cobalt blue dahlia with veined petals and five light green leaves and stem, set on
a white latticinio ground, the sides of the weight cut with six punties. Wide, flat basal flange.
Diam. 3 1/8″ (7.9 cm.)

1965.482.B *(bottom right)* France, Baccarat, c. 1845–50.
Pale yellow pom-pom with green arrow center cane, two long coral and green buds, and seven green leaves and stems, the flower encircled with a ring of alternating white canes and red arrow canes. Six side punties in the Saint-Louis manner. Star-cut base.
Diam. 3 3/16″ (8.1 cm.)

PLATE 43

1965.108.SL *(top left)* France, Saint-Louis, c. 1845–50.
Pelargonium or dog rose with five pink petals with sepals between, mottled yellow and black center, and two long pale green leaves and stem, all over a latticinio ground. Reground. Flat base.
Diam. 2 5/8″ (6.7 cm.)

1965.382.B *(top center)* France, Baccarat, c. 1845–50.
Rose with naturalistic opal pink petals, nine green leaves, and bud. Base star cut. Top and sides reground.
Diam. 3 1/8″ (7.9 cm.)

1965.412.B *(top right)* France, Baccarat, c. 1845–50.
Naturalistic rose and bud with wine red petals together with a small vermilion clematis and eight green leaves and stem, all within a circle of alternating red-centered green and white canes. Star-cut base. Reground.
Diam. 3 3/16″ (8.1 cm.)

1965.479.B *(bottom right)* France, Baccarat, c. 1845–50.
Naturalistic wine red rose and bud together with nine pale green leaves and stem. Star-cut base.
Diam. 2 13/16″ (7.1 cm.)

1965.332.C *(center)* France, Clichy, c. 1845–50.
Pink Clichy rose set on its side, with moss green sepals, stem, and three leaves, and another sprig of five paler acid green leaves, all set over a latticinio ground.
Diam. 3″ (7.6 cm.)

PLATE 44

1965.131.SL *(top left)* France, Saint-Louis, c. 1845–50.
Rare double-blossom fuchsia, the pale pink and blue blossoms on either side of an amber stalk with two buds and six green leaves, set over a latticinio ground.
Diam. 2 15/16″ (7.4 cm.)

1965.83.B *(top right)* France, Baccarat, c. 1845–50.
Cerulean blue buttercup, the cup-shaped outer petals showing white rims, and an inner ring of white petals about a pale yellow rod center; the flower, blue bud, and eight leaves all set in a circle of alternating red-centered green and white canes. Star-cut base.
Diam. 3 3/16″ (8.1 cm.)

1965.77.B *(bottom left)* France, Baccarat, c. 1845–50.
Fringed gentian, the three pink blossoms trimmed with white, the flowers with a bud and six upper and two long lower leaves and stems. Star-cut base.
Diam. 3 1/8″ (7.9 cm.)

1949.80.SL *(bottom right)* France, Saint-Louis, c. 1845–50.
Fuchsia in fuchsia red and blue together with two buds branching from an amber stalk with four green leaves, the stalk entwined with dark threads. Latticinio ground.
Diam. 2 7/8″ (7.3 cm.)

PLATE 45

1965.326.C *(top)* France, Clichy, c. 1845–50.
Sky blue *Convolvulus* (morning glory) lined with white, the large blossom with curving stem and one large green leaf placed over a latticinio ground. Uncommon.
Diam. 2 15/16″ (7.4 cm.)

1965.430.VL *(bottom)* Belgium, Val-Saint-Lambert, 1850–1900.
Rare flower with white underside, the upper surface of the petals with looped bands in pink, cobalt blue, turkey red (vermilion), and pale green, the eight cinnabar green leaves and stem centered within a twisted ribbon of the petal colors. Flat base is star cut. Reground.
Diam. 3 1/16″ (7.8 cm.)

PLATE 46

1965.379.U *(top)* France, undetermined origin, 1870–80.
Large naturalistic chalky pink rose with mottled yellow center, and leaves and stem in two shades of green, the three-dimensional flower placed over a white ground.
Diam. 2 5/8″ (6.7 cm.)

1965.353.U *(bottom)* France, undetermined origin, 1870–80.
Naturalistic white three-dimensional rose with yellow center, two buds, and numerous dark spinach green leaves, the stem a lighter emerald, set upon a cool pink over white ground. Deep basal concavity. Glass light in weight. Reground.
Diam. 2 5/8″ (6.7 cm.)

PLATE 47

1965.357.U France, undetermined origin, c. 1870–80.
Hollow-blown footed weight, the air space containing a realistic white rose with bud, sepals, and leaves. Wide basal rim.
Diam. 3 1/16″ (7.8 cm.)

PLATE 48

1965.75.U *(top)* France, possibly Saint-Louis, 1875–1900.
White dahlia with center of yellow rods and five deep green leaves and stem. Sides reground.
Diam. 2 13/16″ (7.1 cm.)

1965.283.U *(center)* France, possibly Saint-Louis, 1875–1900.
Deep lilac flower with bud and scallop-edged, pale green leaves over a star-cut base, the weight superbly faceted in Saint-Louis style with hollow diamonds.
Diam. 3 1/4″ (8.3 cm.)

1965.212.U *(bottom)* France, possibly Saint-Louis, 1875–1900.
White flower of some relief with yellow rod center and some leaves that resemble those in lizard weights. Deeply cut basal star extends up over sides.
Diam. 3 1/8″ (7.9 cm.)

PLATE 49

1965.134.B *(top)* France, Baccarat, c. 1845–50.
Flat bouquet with three blue-centered, white-veined flowers, a cinnamon red clematis with yellow honeycomb center, and a typical pansy, together with light green leaves and stem. Reground.
Diam. 3″ (7.6 cm.)

1965.165.C *(bottom left)* France, Clichy, c. 1845–50.
Flat bouquet with blue-and-white striped, red, and lilac-colored flower and buds, all in a cornucopia-like form with a birdlike face at the end. Very rare.
Diam. 2 15/16″ (7.4 cm.)

1965.311.SL *(bottom right)* France, Saint-Louis, c. 1845–50.
Flat bouquet with flowers and buds, in pink, tomato, blue, coral, and white, and leaves about
a pink pelargonium, one curving stem emerging. Star-cut base. Reground.
Diam. 3 1/16″ (7.8 cm.)

PLATE 50

1965.469.B *(top left)* France, Baccarat, c. 1845–50.
Magnum flat floral arrangement with a white central buttercup at the axis of a cross, with two
red and two blue flowers at the points, together with leaves, buds, and stems, the blue flowers
having white crow's-feet. Weight cut with one top and six side punties. Star-cut base.
Diam. 3 1/2″ (8.9 cm.)

1965.136.B *(top right)* France, Baccarat, c. 1845–50.
Magnum flat floral bouquet with pale yellow central buttercup, three single flowers (two with
crow's-feet), three small star-centered blue flowers, and leaves and stems. Star-cut base.
Diam. 3 9/16″ (9.1 cm.)

1965.336.B *(bottom)* France, Baccarat, c. 1845–50.
Magnum floral bouquet with two whiskered, crow's-footed pansies and a white clematis,
buds, and light green leaves about a central yellow buttercup. Star-cut base.
Diam. 3 11/16″ (9.4 cm.)

PLATE 51

1965.462.C *(top)* France, Clichy, c. 1845–50.
Magnum natural-looking flat floral bouquet with a variety of flowers and buds in pink, red,
and white, including a viola or pansy, all with numerous green leaves, the stems tied with
a white ribbon. Rare especially in this size.
Diam. 3 3/4″ (9.6 cm.)

1965.389.C *(bottom)* France, Clichy, c. 1845–50.
Natural-looking flat floral bouquet of five flowers, two in blue and three in pink, lilac, and
green, the petals made of canes sliced lengthwise, together with deep green leaves and stems.
Very rare.
Diam. 3″ (7.6 cm.)

PLATE 52

1965.79.C *(top left)* France, Clichy, c. 1845–50.
Flat floral bouquet of white clematis, Clichy rose and two buds, purple flower, and leaves and
stems tied with a white ribbon over a latticinio ground. Some unfused silica and bubbles.
Diam. 2 7/8″ (7.3 cm.)

1965.262.C *(top right)* France, Clichy, c. 1845–50.
Flat floral bouquet of three blue, pink, and purple flowers, with two buds and leaves, the stems
tied with a pink ribbon. Some petals made from canes.
Diam. 2 3/4″ (7 cm.)

1965.383.B *(bottom left)* France, Baccarat, c. 1845–50.
Flat floral bouquet of three red clematis with bud, stems, and leaves. Star-cut base.
Diam. 2 7/8″ (7.3 cm.)

1965.260.VL *(bottom right)* Belgium, probably Val-Saint-Lambert; possibly Venice, 1850–
1900.
Flat floral bouquet of six blue, red, pale yellow, pink, and bright orange flowers and leaves
within a circle of roselike canes and goldstone vines, all on a ground of parallel filigree rods.
Top cut with flat window. Base flat. Glass light in weight.
Diam. 3″ (7.6 cm.)

PLATE 53

1965.199.SL *(bottom left)* France, Saint-Louis, c. 1845–50.
Flat bouquet of four coral, blue, white, and yellow canes and five leaves. Amber-flashed base.
Diam. 2 7/16″ (6.2 cm.)

1965.394.SL *(center)* France, Saint-Louis, c. 1845.
Flat bouquet of three blue and two white canes and five pale green leaves above a fine diamond-cut base.
Diam. 2 7/8″ (7.3 cm.)

1965.384.SL *(top right)* France, Saint-Louis, c. 1845–50.
Miniature flat bouquet of five canes and light green leaves over an amber-flashed, diamond-cut base.
Diam. 1 3/4″ (4.4 cm.)

1965.286.C *(bottom center)* France, Clichy, c. 1845–50.
Miniature flat flower of a single cane with three rich green leaves over a star-cut base, the weight intricately cut with concave diamonds.
Diam. 1 7/8″ (4.7 cm.)

PLATE 54

1965.186.SL(?) France, probably Saint-Louis, c. 1845–50.
Magnum weight faceted in Saint-Louis style of hollow pentagons, the design a flat, single red flower with white center and malachite green leaves, surrounded by spaced millefiori canes over an upset muslin, domed ground backed by long parallel filigree rods in Clichy style. Glass extremely heavy. Refaceted.
Height 3 1/8″ (7.9 cm.); diam. 4 5/16″ (10.9 cm.)

PLATE 55

1965.223.SL *(top left)* France, Saint-Louis, c. 1845–50.
Upright bouquet with two canes and red, white, and blue flowers, the light green leaves arranged more or less like spokes, the bouquet encircled with a clockwise cable torsade in cobalt blue and white. Very small star in flat base.
Diam. 2 13/16″ (7.1 cm.)

1965.237.SL *(top right)* France, Saint-Louis, c. 1845–50.
Upright bouquet with three red, white, and blue, yellow-centered flowers, two canes, and four light green leaves, the bouquet within a torsade with clockwise cobalt blue cable about a filigree twist. Gem-faceted overall with flat triangular and other shaped facets. Star-cut base.
Diam. 2 3/4″ (7 cm.)

1965.58.SL *(center)* France, Saint-Louis, c. 1845–50.
Upright bouquet with central white flower striped blue, yellow, and coral, together with other canes and light green leaves in a spokelike arrangement, all within a broad, clockwise spiral of white threads about a translucent red ring. Flat base cut with a small star. Reground.
Diam. 2 7/8″ (7.3 cm.)

1965.375.SL *(center right)* France, Saint-Louis, c. 1845–50.
Seal or stopper with miniature upright bouquet with four blue, red, and yellow canes about a central white flower, the outer leaves arranged in propeller fashion. Faceted right down to the foot, which appears to have been ground partly away.
Diam. 1 7/16″ (3.7 cm.)

1965.130.SL *(bottom left)* France, Saint-Louis, c. 1845–50.
Upright bouquet with red central flower and other canes and flowers in white and blue, with leaves, all within a clockwise white spiral about a chaplet bead twist, the weight cut with various concave punties and flat gem facets. Star-cut base.
Diam. 3 1/8″ (7.9 cm.)

1965.150.SL *(bottom right)* France, Saint-Louis, c. 1845–50.
Hand cooler with double-headed upright bouquet, its circumference with two yellow and two red-centered white flowers and leaves, the egg-shaped object gem cut with bent diamonds, one end flattened for standing.
Length 2 11/16″ (6.8 cm.)

PLATE 56

1965.661.SL *(top left)* France, Saint-Louis, c. 1845–50.
Upright bouquet with four flowers—white, amber, blue, and red with sulphur center—and six uptilted green leaves, all within a clockwise torsade, the blue spiral thread about a twisted white filigree rod. Deeply star-cut base.
Diam. 3″ (7.6 cm.)

1965.425.SL *(top right)* France, Saint-Louis, c. 1845–50.
Upright bouquet with two canes and three flowers in red, white, and blue, and eight green leaves arranged as spokes, all above an all-white clockwise spiral torsade that appears from the top to cover the whole base, the weight cut, except for the top, with rectangular flat facets.
Diam. 2 13/16″ (7.1 cm.)

1965.466.B *(bottom left)* France, Baccarat, c. 1845–50.
Very rare upright bouquet with numerous buds and canes at various levels about a central arrow cane, the leaves packed in thickly, all above a counterclockwise salmon pink spiral about a gauze cable, the sides gem-cut in flat triangles below the dome. Star-cut base.
Diam. 3 1/16″ (7.8 cm.)

1965.66.SL *(bottom right)* France, Saint-Louis, c. 1845–50.
Upright bouquet dominated by a central pink-veined clematis, the many green leaves arranged as spokes, the weight faceted with three tiers of graduated circular punties about a central top punty. Base cut with small star.
Diam. 3 1/4″ (8.3 cm.)

PLATE 57

1965.70.SL France, Saint-Louis, c. 1845–50.
Upright bouquet dominated by central red flower with yellow center, the other flowers blue and white, and two canes, all with six green leaves above a rare yellow and white clockwise threaded cable; the weight has faceted top and sides with graduated circular punties. Not often seen.
Diam. 2 13/16″ (7.1 cm.)

PLATE 58

1965.454.SL France, Saint-Louis, c. 1845–50.
Extremely rare red over white double overlay (not encased) cut with three tiers of graduated circular punties to reveal an upright bouquet centered by a white flower surrounded by flowers and canes in chartreuse yellow, blue, and red, all with green leaves in a spoke formation. Deeply concave star-cut base. Chip near base reglued.
Diam. 3 3/16″ (8.1 cm.)

PLATE 59

1965.450.SL *(top left)* France, Saint-Louis, c. 1845–50.
Encased pink over white double overlay with seven interior windows enclosing an upright bouquet centered by a blue star-centered red flower, together with other flowers and canes in blue, white, and amber. Star-cut base.
Diam. 3 1/8″ (7.9 cm.)

1965.213.SL *(top right)* France, Saint-Louis, c. 1845–50.
Encased white overlay with seven interior windows enclosing an upright bouquet with a central white yellow-centered flower, and other flowers and canes in coral, amber, blue, and burnt orange, with uptilted green leaves. Star-cut base. Flat basal rim shows no wear. Diam. 3 1/8″ (7.9 cm.)

1965.352.SL *(center)* France, Saint-Louis, c. 1845–50.
Rare encased pink over white double overlay, elaborately cut with trefoils between three oval panels, showing a hare and two hounds, all enclosing an upright bouquet dominated by a red flower with blue cog center, together with green leaves arranged for the most part as spokes. Star-cut base. Basal rim frosted. Diam. 3 3/16″ (8.1 cm.)

1965.98.SL *(bottom left)* France, Saint-Louis, c. 1845–50.
Encased cadmium green over white double overlay with seven interior windows enclosing an off-center upright bouquet in amber, white, and blue with a central red flower and numerous upturned leaves. Flat basal rim shows no wear. Diam. 3 1/8″ (7.9 cm.)

1965.368.SL *(bottom right)* France, Saint-Louis, c. 1845–50.
Encased brilliant royal blue over white double overlay with seven interior windows enclosing a naturalistic upright bouquet with a red, an amber, and a white flower and tightly bunched leaves. Star-cut base. Diam. 2 15/16″ (7.4 cm.)

PLATE 60

1965.161.SL *(top left)* France, Saint-Louis, c. 1845–50.
Five turnips in mauve, amber, white, and red, with green leafage, their tips pointing to the center of a funnel-shaped latticinio basket. Diam. 2 5/8″ (6.7 cm.)

1965.167.SL *(top right)* France, Saint-Louis, c. 1845–50.
Apples, pears and cherries, with leaves casually strewn in delicate funnel-shaped latticinio basket. Top reground. Diam. 2 3/8″ (6 cm.)

1965.225.SL *(center)* France, Saint-Louis, c. 1845–50.
Various fruits, cherries, and leaves casually strewn in a funnel-shaped latticinio basket of thick weave. Top reground. Large center bubble. Diam. 2 15/16″ (7.4 cm.)

1965.242.SL *(bottom left)* France, Saint-Louis, c. 1845–50.
Two delicately colored pears, a peach, four cherries, and leaves strewn in a funnel-shaped latticinio basket. Top reground. Diam. 2 9/16″ (6.5 cm.)

1965.248.SL *(bottom right)* France, Saint-Louis, c. 1845–50.
Fruits and leaves in a funnel-shaped latticinio basket of unusual open weave. Sides reground. Diam. 2 1/2″ (6.3 cm.)

1965.54.SL *(bottom center)* France, Saint-Louis, c. 1845–50.
Pears, cherries, and leaves in a flattened latticinio basket. Diam. 3 1/8″ (7.9 cm.)

PLATE 61

1965.64.SL *(top left)* France, Saint-Louis, c. 1845–50.
Miniature peach and three red cherries with three green leaves. Base mottled. Diam. 1 1/2″ (3.8 cm.)

1965.81.SL *(top)* France, Saint-Louis, c. 1845–50.
Two pears (one greenish yellow and the other apricot-colored), another apricot-colored fruit, three red cherries, and leaves strewn in a funnel-shaped latticinio basket.
Diam. 2 5/8″ (6.7 cm.)

1965.61.SL *(top right)* France, Saint-Louis, c. 1845–50.
Single pear with three leaves. Flat base. Reground.
Diam. 1 3/4″ (4.4 cm.)

1965.120.SL *(bottom left)* France, Saint-Louis, c. 1845–50.
Orange- and-yellow-striped fruit with stem and three green leaves. Flat base. Reground.
Diam. 1 3/4″ (4.4 cm.)

1965.440.SL *(center)* France, Saint-Louis, 1845–50.
Large pear with three red cherries and three green leaves, all in a funnel-shaped latticinio basket.
Diam. 3 1/4″ (8.3 cm.)

1965.185.SL *(bottom right)* France, Saint-Louis, c. 1845–50.
Large yellow pear striped with red on one side and shaded with green on the other, together with four red cherries and four green leaves, all in a funnel-shaped latticinio basket. The weight is cut with six circular side punties. Reground.
Diam. 2 7/8″ (7.3 cm.)

PLATE 62

1965.402.C(?) France, perhaps Clichy (or possibly Saint-Louis), c. 1845–50.
Large naturalistic pear on twigs with leaves, set on a brilliant vermilion ground. Extremely rare. Glass light in weight. Reground.
Diam. 3″ (7.6 cm.)

PLATE 63

1965.256.SL *(top)* France, Saint-Louis, c. 1845–50.
Two strawberries, one pink, one red and smooth, and a yellow-centered white flower on a stalk with four pale green leaves, all set over a latticinio ground.
Diam. 2 1/2″ (6.3 cm.)

1965.329.B *(left)* France, Baccarat, c. 1845–50.
Three strawberries, two of them pink spotted with red, one green spotted with red, on a stalk with seven green leaves. Star-cut base. Reground.
Diam. 3″ (7.6 cm.)

1965.53.SL *(bottom)* France, Saint-Louis, c. 1845–50.
Two pink strawberries and a yellow-centered white flower on a stalk with four light green leaves, all set flush on a flat, single-ply latticinio swirl base. Wide, flat basal rim. Reground.
Diam. 3 3/16″ (8.1 cm.)

PLATE 64

1965.345.SL *(top left)* France, Saint-Louis, c. 1845–50.
Bunch of tiny purple grapes on an orange stalk with two green leaves and yellow tendrils, set on a diamond-scored base, this weight faceted with seven small oval punties and one circular top punty, and below these five large oval punties.
Diam. 2 5/8″ (6.7 cm.)

1965.271.SL *(top right)* France, Saint-Louis, c. 1845–50.
Two bright red cherries on pale yellow stems attached to a pale amber stalk with three light green leaves, the weight cut with three tiers of circular punties.
Diam. 2 3/4″ (7 cm.)

1965.128.SL *(bottom left)* France, Saint-Louis, c. 1845–50.
Bunch of small purple grapes on an orange stalk with pale yellow tendril and two green leaves over diamond-cut base, the sides below the girdle cut with eight concave flattened oval punties.
Diam. 2 15/16″ (7.4 cm.)

1965.145.SL *(bottom right)* France, Saint-Louis, c. 1845–50.
Two violet blue plums on an orange stalk closely bound with green leaves, the top of the weight a flat octagon, the sides cut with flat pentagons of varying shapes. Star-cut base.
Diam. 2 1/2″ (6.3 cm.)

PLATE 65

1965.82.B *(top left)* France, Baccarat, c. 1845–50.
Butterfly with deep ultramarine body, the turquoise eyes and patterned wings within a circle of alternately red and white canes. Star-cut base.
Diam. 3 1/8″ (7.9 cm.)

1965.91.B *(top right)* France, Baccarat, c. 1845–50.
Butterfly with mauve-coated white filigree body, red and white upper and mottled lower wings, and small blue and white eyes hovering over a white clematis with bud, eight pale green leaves, and stem, the weight faceted with seven upper and seven lower circular punties and top punty. Star-cut base.
Diam. 3 1/8″ (7.9 cm.)

1965.455.U *(center)* Possibly Bohemia, 1850–1900.
Miniature paperweight seal with five pale yellow, blue, maroon, orange, and white flowers about a central crimson and white flower, atop a faceted, knopped stem leading to a seal, its base bearing in the Cyrillic alphabet the words "Kramer, Smolensk" about the Gothic initials "C.N." or "C.W." The top and stem appear to have been mated with a wafer of white glass after manufacture.
Height 2 3/4″ (7 cm.); diam. 1 3/4″ (4.4 cm.)

1965.209.B *(bottom left)* France, Baccarat, c. 1845–50.
Butterfly with mauve-coated white filigree body, small blue eyes, and mottled cane-slice wings, hovering over a white clematis, bud, eight green leaves, and stem. Star-cut base.
Diam. 3 1/8″ (7.9 cm.)

1965.91.B *(bottom right)* France, Baccarat, c. 1845–50.
Large butterfly with mauve filigree body, turquoise eyes, mottled cane-slice wings, within a circle of alternately red canes and white canes with blue centers. Flat star-cut base.
Diam. 3 1/4″ (8.3 cm.)

PLATE 66

1965.110.B *(top)* France, Baccarat, c. 1845–50.
A butterfly with mottled wings, the body of mauve-coated white filigree, hovers over a white double clematis with yellow green leaves and bud, the weight gem-faceted with flat pentagons, the top a flat octagon. Flat octagonal base star cut. Probably refaceted, as base shows no wear.
Diam. 2 3/4″ (7 cm.)

1965.406.B *(bottom)* France, Baccarat, c. 1845–50.
A butterfly with deep purple body and mottled wings with blue and white canes in a circle of alternate green and white canes in clear glass, the weight faceted with usual seven punties above but with many smaller facets below that appear to be later cutting, perhaps to remove bruises.
Diam. 3 1/16″ (7.8 cm.)

PLATE 67

1965.199.U *(top left)* Undetermined origin, 20th century.
Butterfly with lemon yellow body and antennae, orange- and white-centered green wings, within a broken circle of four groups of three white canes. Flat star-cut base shows some wear. Glass light in weight.
Diam. 3″ (7.6 cm.)

1965.259.U *(top right)* Undetermined origin, 20th century.
Butterfly with lime green body, yellow eyes, and blue antennae, the blue-centered pink wings made from single canes, the motif flanked by twelve small canes in groups of three. Weight elaborately faceted. Broad star-cut base shows average wear. Glass light in weight.
Diam. 3″ (7.6 cm.)

1965.418.U *(center)* Undetermined origin, probably 20th century.
Enameled butterfly seen in profile, the brown body topped by old rose, blue, and pale yellow wings, the insect lying flat in clear glass, the weight cut with seven large and six small punties. Pontil ground out. Flat basal rim shows inconclusive wear.
Diam. 2 3/4″ (7 cm.)

1965.265.U *(bottom left)* Undetermined origin, 20th century.
Butterfly with blue body and antennae, orange eyes, each orange-centered lilac wing a single cane, in a circle of twelve small red and white canes. Hollow-ground base. Basal rim shows almost no wear. Glass light in weight.
Diam. 2 15/16″ (7.4 cm.)

1965.257.U *(bottom right)* Undetermined origin, 20th century.
Butterfly with pink body and antennae, and mottled wings including Baccarat canes, in a tight circle of small Baccarat-like canes alternately in pink and white over a flat, broadly star-cut base showing minimal wear. Glass light in weight.
Diam. 3 1/8″ (7.9 cm.)

PLATE 68

1965.146.B *(top left)* France, Baccarat, c. 1845–50.
Mottled malachite green snake with vermilion eyes and a large bubble about the head, coiled upon an upset muslin ground, the weight gem-cut with flat top and with flat and concave side cuts. Flat base.
Diam. 3 1/16″ (7.8 cm.)

1965.279.B *(top right)* France, Baccarat, c. 1845–50.
Mottled cerise and green snake with a large bubble in the interstices coiled upon an upset muslin ground, the weight gem-cut with flat top and with flat and concave side cuts. Flat base.
Diam. 3 1/16″ (7.8 cm.)

1965.464.SL *(center)* France, Saint-Louis, c. 1845–50.
Apple green snake with turquoise eyes coiled on a red and white jasper ground.
Diam. 2 3/4″ (7 cm.)

1965.69.B *(bottom left)* France, Baccarat, c. 1845–50.
Mottled bronze over green snake with very deep blue eyes coiled on a rock or sand ground.
Diam. 3 1/8″ (7.9 cm.)

1965.328.B/SL(?) *(bottom right)* France, Baccarat or Saint-Louis, c. 1845–50.
Dusty pink and blue mottled snake with dark-centered white eyes coiled on a green and white jasper ground.
Diam. 3 1/8″ (7.9 cm.)

PLATE 69

1965.447.SL *(top left)* France, Saint-Louis, c. 1845.
Amber squirrel with dark tail and pink nut between paws on an amber branch with three dark translucent green leaves, all within a clockwise spiral red and white filigree cable not visible from above. Fine diamond cut. Flat base.
Diam. 3 3/16″ (8.1 cm.)

1965.112.SL *(top right)* France, Saint-Louis, c. 1845.
Lampwork bird with white, pink-spotted wings, pink tail, and chartreuse yellow legs on a mauve branch with red berries and two translucent leaves, all within a clockwise spiral pink and blue filigree cable. Fine diamond cut. Flat base.
Diam. 3″ (7.6 cm.)

1965.89.B *(bottom)* France, Baccarat, c. 1845–50.
Circular porcelain medallion with a transfer picture in blue of a horse within a blue border, the medallion circled by alternately red and green canes. Flat base shows considerable wear.
Diam. 3 1/4″ (8.3 cm.)

PLATE 70

1965.62.SL *(top left)* France, Saint-Louis, c. 1845–50.
A three-dimensional sulphide fish floats within a circle of typical Saint-Louis canes. Brilliant though sugary; heavy glass.
Diam. 3 1/16″ (7.8 cm.)

1965.297.SL *(top right)* France, Saint-Louis, c. 1845–50.
A three-dimensional sulphide fish with red tongue floats over a mottled red and white jasper ground.
Diam. 2 7/8″ (7.3 cm.)

1965.215.B(?) *(bottom left)* France, possibly Baccarat, probably late 19th century.
Two blown or lampworked white swans, fused to the base of a hollow-blown weight cut with seven circular punties, the footed star-cut base with an internal border of green and white jasper suggesting algae. Flat base shows considerable wear.
Diam. 3 3/16″ (8.1 cm.)

1965.423.B(?) *(bottom right)* France, possibly Baccarat, probably late 19th century.
Three striated lampworked ducks fused to the base of a hollow-blown weight cut with seven circular punties, the footed star-cut base with an internal border of green and white jasper suggesting algae. Flat base shows considerable wear.
Diam. 3 1/8″ (7.9 cm.)

PLATE 71

1965.472.SL *(top)* France, Saint-Louis, c. 1845–50.
Acid-finished, lime green hollow-blown paperweight topped by a mold-cast, three-dimensional, realistic gilded lizard, the gilt partially worn off.
Diam. 3 3/8″ (8.6 cm.)

1965.362.SL *(center)* France, Saint-Louis, c. 1845–50.
A hollow-blown green and white jasper paperweight topped by a gilded three-dimensional molded lizard, the gilt partially worn off.
Diam. 3 3/8" (8.6 cm.)

1965.364.SL *(bottom)* France, Saint-Louis, c. 1845–50.
A hollow-blown white opaline paperweight, cut about the sides with three rows of punties with gilding between the punties, and topped by a gilded three-dimensional molded lizard. Gilt partially worn off.
Diam. 3 3/8" (8.6 cm.)

PLATE 72

1965.458.B *(top)* France, Baccarat, c. 1845–50.
Sulphide portrait of Louis Philippe of France on a deep translucent aquamarine ground, the weight gem-faceted about the sides, the top a flat octagon. Base shows no wear. Refaceted.
Diam. 3 1/2" (8.9 cm.)

1965.341.B *(bottom left)* France, Baccarat, c. 1845–50.
Sulphide head of Napoleon on a translucent cranberry ground, the flat base cut to the edge with a sunburst, the top with one large circular punty, the sides extending slightly below the level of the color ground. Rare.
Diam. 3 3/16" (8.1 cm.)

1965.412.B *(bottom right)* France, probably Baccarat, c. 1845–50.
Luminous sulphide portrait of Lafayette on a deep translucent ultramarine blue ground at the base.
Diam. 2 15/16" (7.4 cm.)

PLATE 73

1965.164.C *(top)* France, Clichy, c. 1845–50.
Sulphide portrait of Benjamin Franklin on a deep opaque cobalt blue ground.
Diam. 2 5/8" (6.7 cm.)

1965.344.C *(top left)* France, Clichy, c. 1845–50.
Sulphide portrait of Napoleon I over a rich opaque thalo blue ground. Reground.
Diam. 3 1/8" (7.9 cm.)

1965.280.C *(top right)* France, Clichy, c. 1845–50.
Sulphide portrait of George Washington over an opaque turquoise blue over white ground. Top and sides reground.
Diam. 3 3/16" (8.1 cm.)

1965.138.B *(center)* France, Baccarat, c. 1845–50.
Sulphide portrait of Lafayette on a translucent lime or peridot green ground, the top of the weight table-cut, the sides faceted in the Baccarat manner for sulphides.
Diam. 3 1/16" (7.8 cm.)

1965.85.B *(bottom left)* France, Baccarat, c. 1845–50.
Sulphide portrait of the Duke of Wellington on a deep opaque ultramarine blue ground over white, the white showing on the underside.
Diam. 3 3/16" (8.1 cm.)

1965.92.B/C(?) *(bottom right)* France, Baccarat or Clichy, c. 1845–50.
Sulphide portrait of George Washington over a deep cobalt over white ground. Carefully reground.
Diam. 3 1/4" (8.3 cm.)

PLATE 74

1965.218.C *(top left)* France, Clichy, c. 1845–50.
Sulphide portrait of Queen Victoria on a very deep opaque amethyst purple (appearing black) ground, top table-cut, sides cut with circular punties alternating with vertical flutes.
Diam. 2 13/16″ (7.1 cm.)

1965.208.SL *(top right)* France, Saint-Louis, c. 1845–50.
Miniature weight with labeled small sulphide of Queen Victoria within a ring of alternating yellow and blue canes over an amber-flashed base. Reground.
Diam. 1 3/4″ (4.4 cm.)

1965.419.U *(bottom left)* Undetermined origin, probably English, perhaps Apsley Pellatt, c. 1840–50.
Sulphide medallion of Queen Victoria in clear glass inscribed about the border "H.M. G.M. QUEEN VICTORIA BORN MAY 24, 1819. CROWNED JUNE 28, 1838. MARRIED FEB 10, 1840."
Diam. 2 1/8″ (5.4 cm.)

1965.343.C *(bottom right)* France, Clichy, c. 1845–50.
Sulphide double portrait of Victoria and Albert on bright thalo blue over white ground. Reground.
Diam. 2 13/16″ (7.1 cm.)

PLATE 75

1965.441.B *(top left)* France, Baccarat, c. 1845–52.
Sulphide profile head of Louis Napoleon Bonaparte over a translucent cranberry footed base. Base star cut. Reground.
Diam. 2 15/16″ (7.4 cm.)

1965.323.SL *(top center)* France, Saint-Louis, c. 1845–50.
Sulphide profile head of Louis Napoleon Bonaparte within a circle of alternately blue and yellow canes, all over an amber-flashed base. Frosted basal rim.
Diam. 2 13/16″ (7.1 cm.)

1965.140.B *(top right)* France, Baccarat, c. 1845–52.
Sulphide profile head of Louis Napoleon Bonaparte on translucent lime green footed base.
Diam. 2 15/16″ (7.4 cm.)

1965.365.SL *(center)* France, Saint-Louis, c. 1845–52.
Three-quarter-view sulphide head marked "Louis Bonaparte" within a circle of alternately green and blue canes over an amber-flashed, fine diamond-cut base, the weight cut with three graduated tiers of flat facets, the flat top with ten sides.
Diam. 3 1/4″ (8.3 cm.)

1965.347.B *(bottom left)* France, Baccarat or possibly Clichy, c. 1845–52.
Sulphide profile head marked "L. N. Bonaparte," half framed in a wreath of green laurel tied with a red ribbon.
Diam. 3 1/16″ (7.8 cm.)

1965.350.B *(bottom center)* France, Baccarat, c. 1845–52.
Sulphide profile head of Louis Napoleon Bonaparte on a footed base with a translucent lime green ground. Refractive index break of some sort.
Diam. 3 1/4″ (8.3 cm.)

1965.405.B *(bottom right)* France, Baccarat, c. 1845–52.
Sulphide profile head of Louis Napoleon Bonaparte on a translucent cranberry ground, the footed weight cut with three tiers of graduated pentagons, the concave top ten-sided.
Diam. 3″ (7.6 cm.)

PLATE 76

1965.407.B *(top)* France, probably Baccarat, c. 1845–50.
Sulphide portrait of William II (1792–1849), king of the Netherlands and grand duke of Luxembourg (1840–1849), framed in a wreath of green laurel tied with a red ribbon.
Diam. 3 1/8" (7.9 cm.)

1965.252.SL *(top left)* France, Saint-Louis, c. 1845–50.
Sulphide portrait of Louis Napoleon within a ring of alternately lime green and blue canes over a fine diamond-cut base. Faceted with seven circular punties.
Diam. 2 15/16" (7.4 cm.)

1965.346.U *(top right)* Undetermined French origin, c. 1845–50.
Sulphide of Comte de Chambord over translucent emerald green ground. Reground.
Diam. 2 11/16" (7.4 cm.)

1965.333.U *(center)* Undetermined English origin, mid-19th century.
Portrait, probably of Prince Albert, in a sulphide medallion edged with laurel and oak branches, set flush with a flat translucent blue ground. Reground. Sulphide perhaps by Allen and Moore.
Diam. 2 5/8" (6.7 cm.)

1965.126.B *(bottom left)* France, Baccarat, c. 1845–50.
A sulphide of the Comte de Chambord on a deep translucent forest green ground.
Diam. 3 3/16" (8.1 cm.)

1965.175.C *(bottom right)* France, Clichy, c. 1845–50.
Sulphide portrait of General Zachary Taylor within a ring of white canes punctuated with red canes on a flat forest green translucent ground.
Diam. 3 1/4" (8.3 cm.)

PLATE 77

1965.457.SL *(top)* France, Saint-Louis, c. 1845–50.
Miniature weight with a small sulphide of Pope Pius IX over an amber-flashed base.
Diam. 2 5/16" (5.9 cm.)

1965.342.SL *(top right)* France, Saint-Louis, c. 1845–50.
Sulphide portrait of Pope Pius IX, so labeled in blue ink on the shoulder, within a ring of green and white canes over a star-cut base.
Diam. 2 7/8" (7.3 cm.)

1965.274.C *(left)* France, Clichy, c. 1845–50.
Sulphide labeled in ink *"ette* MARIE" within a ring of green, red, pink, and white canes, the weight cut with flat facets beneath a raised table.
Diam. 3 3/8" (8.6 cm.)

1965.219.C *(bottom right)* France, Clichy, c. 1845–50.
Sulphide of a mother and child within a ring of white canes punctuated by green canes all on a cobalt blue over white ground.
Diam. 3 1/4" (8.3 cm.)

PLATE 78

1965.460.B *(top left)* France, Baccarat, c. 1845–50.
Half-length sulphide portrait titled "St. Charles" with staff over a flat translucent cranberry ground, the weight gem-cut to just above the base.
Diam. 2 3/4" (7 cm.)

1965.236.B *(top right)* France, Baccarat, c. 1845–50.
Half-length sulphide portrait titled "stte. Marguerite" over a flat translucent cranberry ground, the weight gem-cut to near the base, where a groove makes a foot. Reground.
Diam. 2 3/4" (7 cm.)

1965.276.B *(bottom)* France, Baccarat, c. 1845–50.
Sulphide full-length figure of Joan of Arc with sword and half dressed in armor, her helmet and gauntlet resting on a tree stump, the motif encircled with an oak wreath and placed over a translucent ruby ground. The weight gem-cut with three tiers of flat facets. Flat base.
Diam. 3 1/4" (8.3 cm.)

PLATE 79

1965.465.B France, Baccarat, c. 1845–50.
Magnum magenta over white double overlay cut with twenty-five graduated punties to reveal a sulphide profile portrait of the young Queen Victoria. Deeply star-cut base.
Diam. 3 7/8" (9.9 cm.)

PLATE 80

1965.349.F *(top left)* France, after 1820.
Letterweight containing sulphide portrait of Czar Alexander I of Russia, the sides file cut, the base cut on the bias with strawberry diamonds.
Length 3 1/4" (8.3 cm.)

1965.489.B *(top center)* France, probably Baccarat, 1845–50.
Simulated Legion of Honor medal with ribbon in enameled metal leaf enclosed in a small pendant shape of clear glass.
Length 2 1/16" (5.2 cm.)

1965.484.F *(top right)* France, after 1820.
Sulphide profile portrait, possibly of Duc de Berry, in a rectangular wall plaque with diamond-cut flat base and tooth-cut sides. Has brass ring and clasp.
Length 3 1/16" (7.8 cm.); width 2 1/2" (6.3 cm.)

1965.356.B *(center)* France, probably Baccarat, c. 1845–50.
Simulated Legion of Honor medal with red ribbon in enameled metal leaf reading "BONA-PARTE I CONSUL 1802" in clear glass, base dish shaped.
Diam. 2 1/2" (6.3 cm.)

1965.483.F *(bottom left)* France, after 1820.
Sulphide portrait of Washington in oval wall plaque cut on sides and back with a sunburst and fastened with a bronze doré or ormolu hook and clasp.
Length 4 1/8" (10.5 cm.)

1965.485.F *(bottom right)* France, perhaps Baccarat, after 1820.
Sulphide portrait of Napoleon enclosed in a flattened oval wall plaque, the sides cut in a swirl that becomes a sunburst on the back, the plaque drilled for hanging and fastened with a double loop.
Length 4 3/8" (11.1 cm.)

PLATE 81

1965.374.C France, Clichy, c. 1845–50.
Letterweight, the bottom section a squared paperweight faceted with oval wafers cut between the diamonds, containing a sulphide portrait of Louis Napoleon, the weight tapering up to a miniature paperweight serving as a knob and containing a spaced concentric millefiori arrangement in blue, pink, white, and purple. Flat base, diamond-cut.
Height 3 3/4" (9.6 cm.); lower diam. 3 3/16" (8.1 cm.)

MIXED MEDIA WEIGHTS

PLATE 82

1965.176.B/SL(?) *(top)* France, probably Baccarat or Saint-Louis, c. 1850–78.
Pointing hound in rural landscape reverse etched through deep amber flash on base, giving scene an acid finish. One top and six side punties. Very heavy glass.
Diam. 3 1/4" (8.3 cm.)

1965.358.B/SL(?) *(bottom)* France, probably Baccarat or Saint-Louis, c. 1850–78.
Portrait of Empress Eugénie marked "EUGENIE IMPER*ce*" reverse etched through amber flash on base, giving portrait an acid finish. One top and six side punties. Heavy glass.
Diam. 3 3/16" (8.1 cm.)

PLATE 83

1965.478.EU *(left)* European, latter half 19th century.
Magnum painted weight, the slightly convex porcelain plaque painted with two magenta and blue weighted putti, one with bow and arrow, the other with two white doves and roses, all on a lavender cloud. Weight assembled in the Pinchbeck manner, the synthetic red leather over cardboard cap set in a brass ring and glued to the massive magnifying lens. The plaque is crudely broken into a rough circular shape and on the back is written in ink "5415/T" and in pencilled script "Ea."
Diam. 4 7/16" (11.3 cm.)

1965.192.BO *(top right)* Probably Bohemia, latter half 19th century.
Painted overlay weight, the white glass overlay completely covering the top and sides of the clear glass weight, the dome painted with a large central butterfly surrounded by single blossoms, leaves, and berries, the lower sides gilded with a double band topped by a repeat leaf motif. Base star cut to edge. Glass very light but not hollow blown.
Diam. 2 1/2" (6.3 cm.)

1965.391.BO *(bottom right)* Probably Bohemia, latter half 19th century.
Painted overlay weight, the white glass overlay covering the top and sides of the clear glass weight, the dome painted with large red poppies, yellow roses, and blue flowers and leaves, with faceting of oval punties alternating with vertical flutes near the base. Base star cut to edge. Glass very light but not hollow blown.
Diam. 2 5/8" (6.7 cm.)

PLATE 84

1965.319.E England, possibly Bacchus, c. 1845–51.
A white overlay cut with seven circular punties above six small oval punties alternating with raised diamonds, the overlay continuing over the base. The interior design of leafy green twigs and red and green berries is cut into a quadruple overlay of white over green over white over red. Possibly unique.
Diam. 3 7/16" (8.8 cm.)

PLATE 85

1965.434.P *(top)* European, 2nd half 19th century.
Pinchbeck silver domestic scene in repoussé in an open gallery or porch, with a seated lady instructing a boy who reads or sings from an open book, another female figure behind the chair. Brass base.
Diam. 3 3/16" (8.1 cm.)

1939.63.P *(center)* European, 2nd half 19th century.
Pinchbeck pastoral scene in repoussé relief metal, with a group of figures in colorful costumes standing and sitting by an arbor or trellis, watching a couple dance; hills and a building in the background. Pewter base with six small evenly spaced holes.
Diam. 3" (7.6 cm.)

1965.371.P *(bottom)* European, 2nd half 19th century.
Pinchbeck silver and gold country scene in repoussé relief, a couple on two galloping horses barked at by a dog, the brass base ring with maroon synthetic leather bottom stamped with a gold floral design.
Diam. 3 1/8″ (7.9 cm.)

PLATE 86

1939.26.P *(top)* European, 2nd half 19th century.
Pinchbeck gold repoussé relief head, upper torso of Christ with crown of thorns, bearing the words "ECCE HOMO." Pewter base with two beaded bands.
Diam. 3 5/16″ (8.5 cm.)

1965.372.P *(left center)* European, 2nd half 19th century.
Pinchbeck gold repoussé relief of a hunting scene before a gate, three figures mounted and two others, one standing with a gun, another kneeling by a dog. Pewter base covered with red cloth.
Diam. 3 3/16″ (8.1 cm.)

1965.467.P *(bottom left)* European, 2nd half 19th century.
Pinchbeck domestic scene in gold repoussé relief, with a mother nursing a child, two men, one in pantaloons. Pewter base.
Diam. 3 1/4″ (8.3 cm.)

1965.477.P *(bottom right)* Europe, 2nd half 19th century.
Pinchbeck gold repoussé relief camp scene with several figures mounted and a woman and child on foot. Pewter base covered in worn, faded red velvet.
Diam. 3 1/4″ (8.3 cm.)

CONTINENTAL AND ENGLISH MILLEFIORI

PLATE 87

1965.436.BO *(left)* Bohemia, 1848.
Paperweight vase: this spaced millefiori, including thirteen figure canes and one cane signed and dated "J 1848" all on an upset filigree ground, topped by a white-over-clear-over-translucent cranberry cased vase of trumpet shape with knopped stem, and sides elaborately cut in Bohemian style.
Overall height 6 3/16″ (15.7 cm.); paperweight diam. 2 3/8″ (6 cm.)

1965.243.BO *(right)* Bohemia, c. 1847.
Paperweight vase: the spaced millefiori paperweight including one figure cane on an upset filigree ground, topped by an elongated, urn-shaped white overlay vase elaborately cut in flutes, punties, and hobnail diamonds in Bohemian style. Paper label on base reads: "Purchased in Paris, France, by a prominent Bostonian in 1847."
Overall height 8 5/8″ (21.9 cm.); paperweight diam. 2 7/16″ (6.5 cm.)

PLATE 88

1965.396.VL Belgium, probably Val-Saint-Lambert, after 1883.
Pale translucent yellow over pale translucent pink overlay, weight cut with deep oval punties alternating with deep vertical flutes, enclosing a concentric millefiori design of three cane rows about a circular blue wafer reading in white letters: "NICOLAS FASTRE, IN-GENIEUR HONORAIRE DES MINES." Nicolas Fastré graduated in 1883 from the University of Liège with the degree of Ingénieur Civil des Mines. Flat base.
Diam. 3 9/16″ (9.1 cm.)

PLATE 89

1939.89.W *(top)* England, Whitefriars, 1848.
Inkwell with mushroom-shaped stopper, the base dated 1848, with six concentric rings of canes in pink, green, white, blue, mauve, and green about a central green and white cane, the stopper with four rows of similar canes. Pontil ground out.
Height 5 3/4″ (14.6 cm.); diam. 4 1/16″ (10.3 cm.)

1939.84.W *(bottom left)* England, Whitefriars, 1848.
Low-domed concentric dated 1848, with six rings of canes in blue, yellow, mauve, white, red, and white about a central red and white cane. Pontil mark.
Diam. 3 3/8″ (8.6 cm.)

1965.403.W *(bottom right)* England, Whitefriars, 1848.
Low-domed concentric with four irregular rings of canes in pink and blue, blue, amber, and red about a central mauve and white cane, with traces of the date 1848 in two rods. Pontil mark.
Diam. 3 5/8″ (9.3 cm.)

PLATE 90

1965.405.W England, Whitefriars, 1848.
Inkwell with mushroom-shaped stopper, the base dated 1848 in mauve, and with about six jumbled rows of canes in pink, turquoise, pale green, red, blue, and white, the stopper with a similar assortment. Pontil mark.
Height 5 9/16″ (14.2 cm.); diam. 4 5/8″ (11.8 cm.)

1965.303.BS England, Bacchus, c. 1845-50.
Concentric with four rings of canes in white, crimson lake, and pale cinnabar green, about a central ruffled white cane, the outer ring of crimped green canes tucking under to center of base. Base probably used to drive nails.
Diam. 3 1/4″ (8.3 cm.)

PLATE 91

1965.437.BS England, Bacchus, c. 1845-50.
A garland weight, the red canes in groups enclosed in sodden snow about a central large ruffled white cane, the perimeter of blue-lined cogged canes drawing under to the center of the base.
Diam. 3 5/16″ (8.5 cm.)

PLATE 92

1939.19.BF *(top left)* England, bottle factory, probably 20th century.
Projectile-shaped bottle green weight with footed base showing a two-tiered, frosted flower growing from a pot. Base shows little wear.
Height 5 3/8″ (13.7 cm.); diam. 2 1/4″ (5.7 cm.)

1965.487.BF *(top right)* England, bottle factory after 1829.
Bottle green doorstop decorated with many irregular bubbles about a large mushroom-shaped bubble. Base shows pontil in deep indentation. Heavy wear on basal rim.
Height 4 1/2″ (11.4 cm.); diam. 5″ (12.7 cm.)

1937.752.BF *(bottom)* England, bottle factory, after 1829, and probably late 19th or early 20th century.
A bullet-shaped bottle green weight with nine frosted flowers sprouting from a pot. New-York Historical Society, Folk Art Collection, November 17, 1937.
Height 3 15/16″ (10 cm.); diam. 3 1/4″ (8.3 cm.)

PLATE 93

1965.302.NE *(top)* America, New England Glass Co., c. 1852–80.
Concentric double overlay with three circles of canes in raspberry, turquoise, and yellow about a central rabbit cane, the deep cadmium red over white double overlay cut in Bohemian style with a petal-cut top and quatrefoils about the sides between graduated circular punties in two tiers.
Diam. 2 5/8″ (6.7 cm.)

1965.451.NE *(bottom)* America, New England Glass Co., c. 1852–80.
Spaced concentric double overlay with three rings of pink, cobalt blue, and yellow canes about a central purple and red cane, the apple red over white double overlay cut in Bohemian style with vertical flutes terminating in trefoils between circular punties about the sides, small lozenges about the top punty and at the base. Broken and reglued.
Diam. 3″ (7.6 cm.)

PLATE 94

1965.162.G America, Gillinder & Sons, Philadelphia, c. 1861–80.
Very rare aquamarine blue carpet ground of crimped canes about a central cane of white and blue, the perimeter of white canes tucking in to the center of the base; the weight cut with six deep, long oval punties and circular top punty. Light in weight.
Diam. 3″ (7.6 cm.)

PLATE 95

1965.322.NE *(top)* America, New England Glass Co., c. 1852–80.
Hollow-blown crown of alternating white, gray, and pink and white filigree twists about a central white-blue-pink cane. Pontil not entirely ground away. High dome.
Diam. 2 3/8″ (6 cm.)

1965.327.S *(left)* America, Boston & Sandwich Glass Co., c. 1852–80.
Hollow-blown crown of red, yellow, blue, and white filigree twists and ribbons in random order about a central pink, blue, and white cane. Typical Sandwich profile.
Diam. 2 5/8″ (6.7 cm.)

1965.151.S *(right)* America, probably Boston & Sandwich Glass Co., c. 1852–80.
Hollow-blown crown of red, yellow, green, blue, and white filigree twists and ribbons in random order about a central blue cane. Base drilled.
Diam. 2 5/8″ (6.7 cm.)

1965.99.NE or S *(bottom)* America, New England Glass Co. or Boston & Sandwich Glass Company, c. 1852–80.
Hollow-blown crown of alternating red and blue ribbons, red and white filigree rods and twists about a pale aqua central cane. Base worn and shows pontil mark.
Diam. 2 1/2″ (6.3 cm.)

PLATE 96

1965.244.NE *(left)* America, New England Glass Co., c. 1852–80.
Violet pink poinsettia with five green leaves and stem set on a dish-shaped latticinio ground. Deep basal concavity.
Diam. 3″ (7.6 cm.)

1965.380.NE *(center)* America, probably New England Glass Co., possibly Sandwich, c. 1852–80.
Veined cobalt blue flower with white center and five dark green leaves and stem set flush in a cool pink over white domed ground. Fairly deep basal concavity.
Diam. 2 1/2" (6.3 cm.)

1965.233.S *(top right)* America, probably Sandwich, c. 1852–80.
Bright pink flower with white center and substantial veined bud with two green leaves over a convex, finely woven latticinio ground.
Diam. 2 1/2" (6.3 cm.)

1965.84.S *(bottom right)* America, Boston & Sandwich Glass Co., c. 1852–80.
White poinsettia with numerous bubbles between petals and five emerald green leaves. Pristine dome.
Diam. 2 15/16" (7.4 cm.)

PLATE 97

1965.166.NE *(left)* America, New England Glass Co., c. 1852–80.
Rare, pale salmon pink camomile or pom-pom with fluffy petals contained in a white-lined green cup, with five dark green leaves and stem set above a funnel-shaped latticinio basket identical to the basket in the weight at top center. One petal detached. Deep basal concavity.
Diam. 2 7/16" (6.2 cm.)

1965.432.NE *(top center)* America, New England Glass Co., c. 1852–80.
Rare white camomile or pom-pom with fluffy petals, pale aqua center, and five deep emerald green leaves and stem, set above a funnel-shaped latticinio basket identical to the basket in the weight at left. Flat basal rim, acid-finished. Pontil mark.
Diam. 2 1/2" (6.3 cm.)

1965.360.S *(right)* America, Boston & Sandwich Glass Co., c. 1852–80.
Pink poinsettia with five neat bubbles between the five inner petals, about a pink and green center cane, with two green leaves and stem. Typically off center to left. Shallow basal concavity. Light in weight.
Diam. 2 5/16" (5.9 cm.)

1965.220.NE *(bottom)* America, New England Glass Co., c. 1852–80.
White buttercup with orange and yellow center and two rows of petals together with five neat green leaves, set flush in an extremely finely powdered, pink jasper ground. Very deep basal concavity.
Diam. 2 7/8" (7.3 cm.)

PLATE 98

1965.453.NE *(top left)* America, New England Glass Co., c. 1852–80.
Magnum cross composed of mulberry-colored petals about a brilliant turquoise center cane, the cross held on the underside by green stems, all over a pale, saucer-shaped latticinio ground open in the center. Deep basal concavity. Pontil not entirely ground away.
Diam. 3 1/2" (8.9 cm.)

1965.313.NE *(top right)* America, New England Glass Co., c. 1852–80.
Magnum cross composed of mulberry-colored petals about a red-white-blue center cane, the cross held on the underside by green stems, all over a saucer-shaped latticinio ground. Deep basal concavity. Irregular rim.
Diam. 3 5/16" (8.5 cm.)

1965.420.NE *(bottom)* America, New England Glass Co., c. 1852–80.
Three groups of five green, eggplant, and pink leaves with a center cane and canes between the groups, all over a convex latticinio ground. Deep basal concavity. Irregular rim.
Diam. 3 3/4" (9.6 cm.)

PLATE 99

1965.298.NE America, New England Glass Co., c. 1852–80.
Very rare cocoa over white double overlay cut in Bohemian style, with three tiers of long oval and circular punties with clover cuts between, and closely placed vertical flutes above the base; the motif a flat bouquet with three bright canes and malachite green leaves set flush in bollard-shaped white dome, all within ring of coral, white, and blue canes. Base concave.
Diam. 3 1/8″ (7.9 cm.)

PLATE 100

1965.109.NE *(top)* America, New England Glass Co., c. 1852–80.
Upright red, white, and blue bouquet with emerald green leaves in latticinio basket. Base shows pontil mark. Top reground.
Diam. 2 5/16″ (7.4 cm.)

1965.198.NE *(left)* America, New England Glass Co., c. 1852–80.
Upright red, white, and blue bouquet with emerald green leaves in funnel-shaped latticinio basket. Bouquet off center. Deep basal concavity.
Diam. 2 3/4″ (7 cm.)

1965.117.NE *(right)* America, New England Glass Co., c. 1852–80.
Upright red, white, and blue bouquet with emerald green leaves in latticinio funnel-shaped basket. Deep basal concavity. Glass swirly.
Diam. 2 5/8″ (6.7 cm.)

1965.415.NE *(bottom)* America, New England Glass Co., c. 1852–80.
Two realistically lampworked pink roses and bud with puckered green leaves over delicate latticinio. Several trapped bubbles. Pontil mark on base. Glass slightly amber-tinted.
Diam. 2 7/8″ (7.3 cm.)

PLATE 101

1965.147.NE *(top)* America, New England Glass Co., c. 1852–80.
Magnum upright floral bouquet with bright canary yellow, cobalt blue, red, and mauve blossoms, a white bud, a cherry, two pears, and naturalistic leaves, all set over a large funnel-shaped latticinio basket. Concave base has large flat rim.
Diam. 3 15/16″ (10 cm.)

1965.304.NE *(bottom)* America, New England Glass Co., c. 1852–80.
Brilliant upright bouquet, the coral, white, blue, purple, and yellow flowers symmetrically about a red central flower, all set over a delicate, pale latticinio ground; the weight entirely cut about the sides with graduated hollow diamonds. Deep basal concavity. Irregular rim.
Diam. 2 3/4″ (7 cm.)

PLATE 102

1965.188.NE America, New England Glass Co., c. 1852–80.
Rare magnum floral spray dominated by a lemon yellow and a blue flower, with smaller blossoms in red, mauve, yellow, and white, together with leaves, the stems bound with yellow ribbon, all over a funnel-shaped latticinio ground; the weight gem-faceted in three tiers of flat triangles. Wide flat basal rim.
Diam. 3 3/4″ (9.6 cm.)

PLATE 103

1965.452.NE America, New England Glass Co., c. 1852–80.
Extremely rare upright bouquet of small-veined blue flowers, canes, leaves, set low down in a white saucer; the raspberry red over white double overlay is elaborately cut like a melon or squash. Vertical panels cut with leaves alternate with tall vertical flutes. Chipped.
Diam. 2 5/8″ (6.7 cm.)

PLATE 104

1965.277.MW *(top)* America, Mt. Washington Glass Co., c. 1870–90.
Magnum weight with a large salmon-colored dahlia, the center composed of small upright petals, with five dew-speckled acid green leaves and stem. Base shows pontil mark with waffle pattern. Annealing crack over one leaf.
Diam. 3 13/16″ (9.8 cm.)

1965.309.MW *(bottom)* America, Mt. Washington Glass Co., c. 1870–90.
Magnum weight with a large rose with many small mottled pink petals and five dew-speckled acid green leaves and stem. Large bubble under flower. Base shows pontil mark with waffle pattern.
Diam. 4 1/16″ (10.3 cm.)

PLATE 105

1965.331.MW America, Mt. Washington Glass Co., c. 1870–90.
Magnum weight with very large naturalistic rose with white tipped pink petals, two buds, five dew-speckled malachite green leaves and stem. Deep basal concavity. Pontil mark shows pattern of small squares.
Diam. 4 5/16″ (10.9 cm.)

PLATE 106

1965.337.NE *(bottom)* America, probably New England Glass Co., c. 1852–80.
Very rare lampwork parrot with red wing, blue beak and eye, pink head, and blue over pink body, on a branch of three green leaves, all over a flat latticinio ground. Pontil mark, many bubbles. High crown.
2 13/16″ (7.1 cm.)

1965.312.NE *(center)* America, New England Glass Co., c. 1852–80.
Very rare rose tree with pink and pale yellow roses mixed with green leaves atop an orange yellow stalk. Deep basal concavity and basal rim typically irregular. Reground.
Diam. 3″ (7.6 cm.)

1965.104.NE *(top)* America, New England Glass Co., c. 1852–80.
Very rare apricot-colored bird with deep colored thin beak and eye, yellow wing and tail, on a branch of three leaves. Deep basal concavity and rim typically irregular. Reground.
Diam. 2 15/16″ (7.4 cm.)

PLATE 107

1965.309.NE *(top)* America, New England Glass Co., c. 1852–80.
Symmetrical fruit arrangement of five apples and four cherries and leaves in funnel-shaped latticinio basket. Deep basal concavity.
Diam. 2 1/2″ (6.3 cm.)

1965.442.NE *(center)* America, New England Glass Co., c. 1852–80.
Symmetrical fruit arrangement of five apples and four cherries and leaves in a funnel-shaped latticinio basket. Deep basal concavity and irregular basal rim.
Diam. 2 5/8″ (6.7 cm.)

1965.148.NE *(bottom left)* America, New England Glass Co., c. 1852–80.
Symmetrical fruit arrangement of five apples and four cherries and leaves in a funnel-shaped latticinio basket. Deep basal concavity and punty crack.
Diam. 3″ (7.6 cm.)

1965.357.S or NE *(bottom right)* America, Sandwich or New England Glass Co., c. 1852–80.

Three red berries suspended from a twig of five leaves over an openly woven latticinio ground. Base shows pontil mark.
Diam. 2 3/4″ (7 cm.)

PLATE 108

1965.52.MW *(top)* America, Mt. Washington Glass Co., c. 1870–90.
Magnum weight with five crimson strawberries, each on leaves, with yellow-centered white blossoms and leaves between the berries. Flat base showing pontil crack. Also an annealing crack under the two berries.
Diam. 4″ (10.2 cm.)

1965.246.S *(right)* America, Boston & Sandwich Glass Co., c. 1852–80.
Two blue plums on stems from a stalk with four pale green leaves. Pristine dome. Typical Sandwich profile. Glass light in weight.
Diam. 2 3/4″ (7 cm.)

1965.373.S *(bottom)* America, Boston & Sandwich Glass Co., c. 1852–80.
Five pink cherries on stems from a stalk with five pale green leaves. Reground.
Diam. 2 15/16″ (7.4 cm.)

PLATE 109

1965.203.NE *(top left)* America, New England Glass Co., c. 1860–80.
Large blown pear shading from deep amber red to yellow green with dark green blossom, fused stem down to "cookie" base. Fruit indented in one place. Broken.
Base diam. 3″ (7.6 cm.)

1937.751.NE *(top right)* America, New England Glass Co., c. 1860–80.
Small blown pear in Burmese pink with dark green blossom and stem, fused to "cookie" base. Tip of stem missing.
Base diam. 2 9/16″ (6.5 cm.)

1965.73.NE *(bottom left)* America, New England Glass Co., c. 1860–80.
Fine large blown apple, brown and pale yellow striped with reddish brown and fused upside down to "cookie" base, the dark green blossom showing on top. Broken.
Base diam. 3 5/8″ (9.3 cm.)

1965.316.NE *(bottom right)* America, New England Glass Co., c. 1860–80.
Small blown apricot with clear glass blossom fused stem down to "cookie" base, the fruit split along the seam.
Base diam. 2 1/8″ (5.4 cm.)

PLATE 110

1965.60.NE *(top)* America, New England Glass Co., c. 1860–80.
Small blown red and yellow pear with dark green blossom fused stem down to "cookie" base.
Base diam. 2 3/4″ (7 cm.)

1965.118.NE *(left)* America, New England Glass Co., c. 1860–80.
Blown pink and pale yellow apple with dark green blossom fused to "cookie" base.
Base diam. 2 13/16″ (7.1 cm.)

1965.124.NE *(right)* America, New England Glass Co., c. 1860–80.
Small blown deep pink and pale yellow pear with dark green blossom fused stem down to "cookie" base.
Base diam. 2 13/16″ (7.1 cm.)

1965.292.NE *(bottom)* America, New England Glass Co., c. 1860–80.
Large rose red fading to pink blown apple with dark green blossom fused stem down to "cookie" base.
Base diam. 3 1/16" (7.8 cm.)

PLATE III

1965.135.U *(top)* Perhaps France, c. 1850.
Sulphide portrait labeled "Lafayette" in blue ink on pale translucent cranberry ground. Top reground.
Diam. 2 3/4" (7 cm.)

1965.378.U *(top left)* Undetermined origin, perhaps English, c. 1850.
Sulphide portrait of Prince Albert on a deep translucent cobalt ground. Top reground.
Diam. 2 1/2" (6.3 cm.)

1965.438.U *(top right)* Undetermined origin, perhaps Clichy, c. 1850.
Sulphide double portrait labeled in blue ink "Victoria-Albert," on a pale translucent cranberry ground with dichroic overtones.
Diam. 2 3/4" (7 cm.)

1965.267.U *(center)* Undetermined origin, c. 1850.
Sulphide bust of General Zachary Taylor labeled in blue ink "Taylor" on a deep translucent cobalt ground.
Diam. 2 5/8" (6.7 cm.)

1965.282.U *(bottom left)* Undetermined origin, c. 1845–50.
Sulphide portrait labeled in blue ink "Washington" on a pale translucent mauve ground.
Diam. 2 5/8" (6.7 cm.)

1965.432.U *(bottom right)* Undetermined origin, perhaps Clichy, c. 1850.
Sulphide double portrait of Victoria and Albert over opaque cobalt blue over white ground. Top partially reground.
Diam. 2 7/8" (7.3 cm.)

PLATE 112

1965.156.M *(left)* America, Whitall Tatum & Co., Millville, N. J., early 20th century.
Yellow-centered water lily with pink tuberous petals, another group of white petals, and leaves, in a sphere of clear glass on footed base. Pontil ground out.
Diam. 3 13/16" (9.8 cm.)

1965.426.M *(top)* America, Whitall Tatum & Co., Millville, N.J., early 20th century.
Saffron yellow wineglass-shaped rose without leaves in clear glass sphere over footed base. Base shows pontil mark.
Diam. 3 11/16" (9.4 cm.)

1965.263.M *(bottom)* America, Whitall Tatum & Co., Millville, N.J., early 20th century.
Pink opal rose with three green over white leaves in clear glass sphere over footed base. Pontil mark.
Diam. 3 5/8" (9.3 cm.)

PLATE 113

1965.178.M *(top left)* America, Whitall Tatum & Co., Millville, N.J., early 20th century.
Bright canary yellow rose with four green leaves in sphere of clear glass with footed base.
Base diam. 3 3/8" (8.6 cm.)

1965.206.M *(top right)* America, Whitall Tatum & Co., Millville, N.J., early 20th century. Well-formed opal pink rose with three green leaves in a clear glass sphere lacking the foot. Flat base.
Diam. 3 7/16" (8.8 cm.)

1965.179.M *(bottom left)* America, Whitall Tatum & Co., Millville, N.J., early 20th century. Apricot-colored rose with four emerald leaves in a sphere of clear glass on a footed base showing a cloverleaf pontil mark.
Diam. 3 5/8" (9.3 cm.)

1965.351.M *(bottom right)* America, Whitall Tatum & Co., Millville, N.J., early 20th century. Pale pink rose with three malachite green leaves in a sphere of clear glass on a footed base. Base shows pontil mark.
Diam. 3 3/4" (9.6 cm.)

PLATE 114

1965.207.M *(top left)* America, Whitall Tatum & Co., Millville, N.J., early 20th century. White rose with three pale green leaves in clear glass sphere with basal foot. Base flat and frosted.
Diam. 3 9/16" (9.1 cm.)

1965.386.M *(top right)* America, Whitall Tatum & Co., Millville, N.J., early 20th century. Pink opal magnolia-like flower with long petals and three emerald green leaves in sphere with basal foot. Base shows pontil mark.
Diam. 3 5/8" (9.3 cm.)

1965.422.M *(bottom left)* America, made by Charles Kaziun, Brockton, Mass., after 1940. Deep pink opal rose with four bright green leaves in clear glass sphere with basal foot. Cane seen from underside shows letter "K." Base shows pontil mark. Reground.
Diam. 2 1/4" (5.7 cm.)

1965.366.M *(bottom right)* America, Whitall Tatum & Co., Millville, N.J., early 20th century. Pink opal rose with four translucent emerald green leaves in clear glass sphere on footed base. Pontil mark shows an X or cloverleaf pattern.
Diam. 3 5/8" (9.3 cm.)

PLATE 115

1965.413.M *(left)* America, Millville, N.J., possibly made by Charles Pepper at Whitall Tatum & Co., or at the T. C. Wheaton Co., c. 1900–20.
A dusky, cinnamon red rose and eight green over white leaves tilted in a sphere of limpid clear glass above a baluster stem and flat pad foot. Pontil mark on base.
Height 5 7/8" (14.9 cm.); diam. of sphere 3 11/16" (9.4 cm.)

1965.294 *(right)* America, Whitall Tatum & Co., Millville, N. J., probably made by Ralph Barber, early 20th century.
Crocus weight on conical, high-kick base, the opal white blossom streaked with color and goldstone. Pontil mark on base.
Height 4 1/2" (11.4 cm.); paperweight diam. 3" (7.6 cm.)

PLATE 116
1965.141.MW/S (?) *(left)* America, early 20th century, possibly Mt. Washington or Union Glass Co. in Somerville.
A flattened dome on hollow baluster stem and flat foot, the motif a flat pink poinsettia dotted with goldstone and five green leaves and stem. Brilliant glass. Base shows pontil.
Height 6 1/8" (15.5 cm.); paperweight diam. 3 11/16" (9.4 cm.)

1965.300.M *(right)* America, Millville, N.J., early 20th century, possibly made by Michael Kane.
A flat motif with cross entwined with vines, rocks, and grass in pink, brown, and green, standing upright in a sphere cut with five deep circular punties all on a baluster stem and flat pad foot. Pontil ground out.
Height 5 1/2″ (14 cm.); paperweight diam. 3 1/2″ (8.9 cm.)

PLATE 117

1965.398.M *(left)* America, Whitall Tatum & Co., Millville, N.J., possibly made by Michael Kane, c. 1900.
White sailboat sloop with railing and red flag in green, bubbly waves, all upright in a large punty-cut sphere with footed base. Large pontil mark. Can be looked at from either side.
Height 4 1/4″ (10.8 cm.); diam. 3 5/8″ (9.3 cm.)

1965.315.M *(right)* America, Whitall Tatum & Co., Millville, N.J., possibly made by Michael Kane, c. 1900.
White horse with long tail on blue green grass, all upright in a large punty-cut sphere with footed base. Pontil mark.
Height 4 1/4″ (10.8 cm.); diam. 3 5/8″ (9.3 cm.)

PLATE 118

1965.181.SO *(bottom)* America, Union Glass Co., Somerville, Mass., c. 1900–20.
Three opaque white pigs and a red, a blue, and a white flower with green leaves on a colored chip ground. Very clear and heavy glass. Concave base.
Diam. 4 5/8″ (11.8 cm.)

1965.182.SO *(top)* America, Union Glass Co., Somerville, Mass., c. 1900–20.
A red and white and a green and white bird at a green nest with white eggs on a ground of chips and strands of colored glass. Very heavy brilliant glass. Concave base.
Diam. 4 1/8″ (10.5 cm.)

PLATE 119

1965.230.T America, Tiffany, after February 20, 1904.
Doorstop-size Tiffany paperweight, the large pale green mass shaped like a gather of glass, on a plain foot. The internal motif shows two sea lettuce green translucent fish swimming among delicate iridescent fronds. Basal flange signed "1984H L.C. Tiffany. Favrile."
Height 6 1/8″ (15.5 cm.); diam. about 4 3/4″ (12.1 cm.)

PLATE 120

1965.435.Y *(top)* Scotland, by Paul Ysart, c. 1940–60.
Flat group of pink, blue, and lavender flowers flanked by two green leaves within a circle of green, amber and white canes, all sunk in a mulberry black ground. Pontil mark.
Diam. 3 3/8″ (8.6 cm.)

1965.310.Y *(center)* Scotland, by Paul Ysart, c. 1940–60.
An amber-bodied butterfly with millefiori wings in blue, green, and pink canes mixed with white, all on a deep blue opaque ground. Pontil mark. Heavy and perhaps artificially induced wear.
Diam. 3 1/4″ (8.3 cm.)

1965.290.Y *(bottom)* Scotland, by Paul Ysart, c. 1940–65.
Flat bouquet of flowers with leaves, tied with a red aventurine ribbon, a tiny rod in the center of the pink flower signed PY all sunk in a deep cobalt ground. Pontil mark. Reground.
Diam. 2 7/8″ (7.3 cm.)

1939.57.SL France, Saint-Louis, c. 1845–50.
Scrambled weight with fragments of colored, twisted ribbon, including aventurine ribbon, filigree, and canes including a figure cane.
Diam. 2 1/4" (5.7 cm.)

1939.87.SL France, Saint-Louis, c. 1845–50.
Scrambled weight with a jumble of cane, filigree, and ribbon fragments including yellow aventurine ribbon. Top scratched.
Diam. 2 3/16" (5.6 cm.)

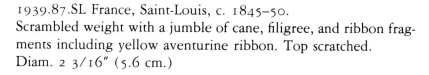

1965.555.B France, Baccarat, c. 1845–50.
Scrambled weight with filigree twists in red, white, blue, and green set at right angles to one another.
Diam. 3 1/8" (7.9 cm.)

1939.79.U Undetermined origin, c. 1920–30.
A close millefiori of crudely colored canes over a green aventurine and chip ground. Flat base.
Diam. 2 7/8" (7.3 cm.)

(lacks number) China, after 1930.
Scrambled weight of sliced cane and filigree in pink, yellow, blue, and green.
Diam. 2 3/16" (5.6 cm.)

1939.50.CH China, 20th century to today.
Three-pronged curving form with millefiori design.
Length 2 3/4" (7 cm.)

1965.322.C France, Clichy, c. 1845–50.
Millefiori concentric of five rows of close-packed canes in pale green, pink, cobalt blue, and white about four blue canes enclosed by a blue and white stave basket.
Diam. 2 1/4" (5.7 cm.)

1965.266.NE America, New England Glass Co., c. 1852–80.
A spaced concentric with blue, pink, green, and white canes on open latticinio ground. Deep basal concavity.
Diam. 2 1/2" (6.3 cm.)

1939.38.VL Belgium, probably Val-Saint-Lambert, late 19th, early 20th century.
Spaced concentric on mottled white cushion ground, the small canes including numerous Clichy-like roses. Pontil ground out.
Diam. 3 1/2" (8.9 cm.)

1939.48.GE Germany, early 20th century.
A concentric with two rows of orange and blue canes about a central red and white cane, all over a chip ground. Flat base.
Diam. 2 1/8" (5.4 cm.)

1943.112.GE Germany, early 20th century.
Millefiori concentric with two rows of mustard yellow, red, and turquoise canes about a central red cane, all on a chip ground.
Diam. 2 1/4" (5.7 cm.)

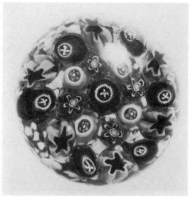

1939.58.GE Germany, late 19th or 20th century.
A concentric millefiori, the green and white and blue canes about a central red and yellow cane, all on a speckled ground. Flat acid-finished or ground base.
Diam. 2 1/2" (6.3 cm.)

1939.94.GE Germany, late 19th or early 20th century.
A concentric millefiori with two rings of blue and yellow-red-white canes about an orange- and white-spotted dark cane. Flat acid-finished base, faintly acid-etched "Made in Germany."
Diam. 2 1/4" (5.7 cm.)

1939.84.B France, Baccarat, probably c. 1930.
A miniature concentric with a circle of yellow canes within a circle of alternating red, white, and blue canes about a central red and white cane with stars. Probably by Dupont.
Diam. 1 7/8" (4.7 cm.)

1939.76.CH China, c. 1930s.
A concentric millefiori weight with red-centered green and white canes about a green-centered red and white cane. Roughened flat base. Glass greasy to the touch.
Diam. 2 1/8" (5.4 cm.)

1939.33.B France, Baccarat, c. 1930s.
Dupont garland of six pink and white circles of canes about a central yellow circle and red center cane. Dupont profile. Base shows little wear.
Diam. 2 1/2" (6.3 cm.)

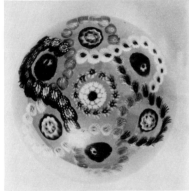

1939.67.B France, Baccarat, c. 1930.
Dupont garland of six variously colored loops enclosing six canes about a central cane and ring. Canes blurred. Dupont profile. Medium basal wear.
Diam. 2 3/4" (7 cm.)

1939.72.B France, Baccarat, by Dupont, c. 1930.
A modern garland weight in pink, yellow, and blue with a central arrow or crow's-foot cane as a flower, the heart-shaped garlands enclosing deep rose-colored canes. Shows Dupont profile and styling.
Diam. 2 7/8" (7.3 cm.)

1939.55.CH China, 1930–40.
Flattened triple cushion in green and white but watery latticinio, with central pink cane in flattened-domed, low-profile weight. Glass slightly greasy to the touch. Base cut flat.
Diam. 2" (5.1 cm.)

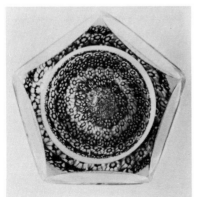

1965.596.V Probably Scotland, Vasart Co., c. 1950.
A modern paperweight punty cut in Clichy style with a concentric mushroom, the rings in pink, orange, baby blue, and green.
Diam. 2 3/8" (6 cm.)

1965.45.SL France, Saint-Louis, c. 1953.
Modern turquoise over white double overlay, cut with six punties to reveal a close millefiori mushroom, the base star cut.
Diam. 3 1/4″ (8.3 cm.)

1965.566.U Undetermined origin, 20th century.
A modern crown weight of filigree twists and ribbons in red, green, pink, blue, and white, lacking a central cane, the sides and top with punties. Concave base shows little wear.
Diam. 3″ (7.6 cm.)

1965.337.B France, Baccarat, c. 1845–50.
A typical small Baccarat pansy with eggplant upper petals and eggplant spotted lower petals and five green leaves. Star-cut base.
Diam. 2 1/8″ (5.4 cm.)

1965.516.B France, Baccarat, c. 1845–50.
Typical well-done Baccarat pansy with eggplant upper petals and eggplant spotted yellow lower petals with ten green leaves and bud. Star-cut base.
Diam. 2 7/8″ (7.3 cm.)

1965.612.B France, probably Baccarat, c. 1850.
A four-leaf clover, the leaves imprinted with veins. High-domed top partially reground. Very heavy glass.
Diam. 3 3/16″ (8.1 cm.)

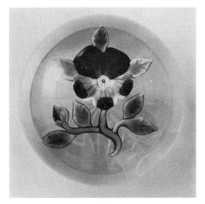

1939.41.B France, Baccarat, by Dupont, c. 1930.
Dupont pansy with typical amber petals over star-cut base. Shows Dupont profile. Little basal wear.
Diam. 2 7/8" (7.3 cm.)

1939.61.B France, Baccarat, c. 1930.
A Baccarat pansy with three chrome yellow lower petals, five green leaves and stem over a star-cut base. Probably made by Dupont.
Diam. 2 1/4" (5.7 cm.)

1939.78.B France, Baccarat, c. 1930.
Dupont pansy with typical ocher-amber petals on star-cut base. Shows Dupont profile.
Diam. 2 7/8" (7.3 cm.)

1965.132.B France, Baccarat, c. 1930.
Dupont pansy with leaves over star-cut base, a white lozenge bearing the faked spurious date 1853. Wear on base faked.
Diam. 2 7/8" (7.3 cm.)

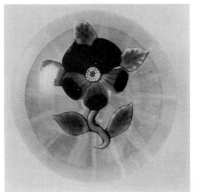

1965.324.B France, Baccarat, c. 1930.
A Dupont pansy with amber flower petals and five green leaves. Dupont profile. Star-cut base shows little wear.
Diam. 2 1/8" (5.4 cm.)

1965.126.B France, Baccarat, c. 1845–50.
A Baccarat primrose, the red petals looped with white, and eleven green leaves and stem over a star-cut base. Two perforations in petals. Dome slightly flattened by regrinding.
Diam. 2 5/8″ (6.7 cm.)

1965.576.S America, Boston & Sandwich Glass Co., c. 1852–80.
A pink poinsettia with pink and white cane center and five serrated green leaves and stem slightly off center to the right in clear glass. Original condition but top worn.
Diam. 3″ (7.6 cm.)

1965.202.NE America, New England Glass Co., c. 1852–80.
A blue poinsettia on a latticinio ground bordered with six purple and green moths. Typical irregular, deeply concave base.
Diam. 3 1/4″ (8.3 cm.)

1965.282.SL France, Saint-Louis, c. 1845–50.
A pink dahlia with five green leaves and yellow and blue center cane. Star-cut base heavily worn and bruised. Reground.
Diam. 2 1/4″ (5.7 cm.)

1939.77.SL France, Saint-Louis, c. 1845–50.
Tricolor flat bouquet with three flowers, stems, and four green leaves. Rare.
Diam. 2 3/4″ (7 cm.)

1965.458.U Undetermined origin, after 1930.
Modern weight with four pink and yellow lampwork flowers and leaves on long stems, rising over a mottled green ground. Flat base shows some wear.
Diam. 3 1/4" (8.3 cm.)

1965.139.SL France, Saint-Louis, c. 1845–50.
A good Saint-Louis fruit weight, the apple, pear, cherries strewn casually in a fine latticinio basket. Reground top. Base shows Clichy frosting.
Diam. 3" (7.6 cm.)

1965.149.SL France, Saint-Louis, c. 1845–50.
A peach with three light green leaves in clear glass.
Diam. 2 13/16" (7.1 cm.)

1965.258.SL France, Saint-Louis, c. 1845–50.
A typical Saint-Louis scattered fruit weight in latticinio basket, except that the coloring is darkened, perhaps from overfiring.
Diam. 2 9/16" (6.5 cm.)

1965.67.C France, probably Clichy, c. 1845–50.
A sulphide of Benjamin Franklin in clear glass of typical Clichy profile.
Diam. 3 1/8" (7.9 cm.)

1965.138.F France, factory unknown, late 19th century.
Sulphide portrait of Sadi Carnot on a deep rose over white ground, the color ground cracked. Low dome but not reground. Pontil mark on base. Carnot was president of the French Republic from 1887 until 1894, when he was assassinated.
Diam. 2 7/8″ (7.3 cm.)

1965.463.B/C(?) France, possibly Baccarat or Clichy, c. 1858.
A sulphide American flag with thirteen stripes but with thirty-two stars arranged in the shape of a star, on a deep ultramarine over white ground cut with one top punty and six side punties. Concave base. As of July 4, 1858, Minnesota became the 32nd state, but no star-shaped arrangement appears on the flag of that date.
Diam. 3 1/16″ (7.8 cm.)

1965.622.U Possibly France or Belgium, mid-19th century.
A sulphide portrait of Saint-Louis on cobalt blue over white ground, the top of the weight cut with facets.
Diam. 3 1/16″ (7.8 cm.)

1965.159.U Undetermined origin, possibly America, c. 1854.
Sulphide portrait of Louis Kussuth, Hungarian revolutionary and patriot. Impressed into the back of the sulphide are the words, "L.K. Governor of Hungaria. Set at liberty by the People of the United States of America 1851" (or 1854).
Diam. 2 3/4″ (7 cm.)

1965.166.C(?) France, possibly Clichy, c. 1845–50.
Sulphide three-quarter-view portrait of General Zachary Taylor in uniform. Reground.
Diam. 3 3/16″ (8.1 cm.)

1965.221.C(?) France, perhaps Clichy, mid-19th century.
A sulphide of General Zachary Taylor (inscribed "Taylor" in blue ink) on a translucent, almost dichroic pink ground with yellow overtones. Top deeply reground. Concave base, irregular rim.
Diam. 2 13/16" (7.1 cm.)

1965.396.U Undetermined origin, perhaps America, 3rd quarter 19th century.
A sulphide bust of General Zachary Taylor inscribed "Taylor" in ink, on a pale translucent mauve ground.
Diam. 2 5/8" (6.7 cm.)

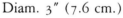

1948.397.NE America, New England Glass Co., after 1851.
Flat hexagonal weight showing an acid-finished portrait titled "Henry Clay" pressed intaglio into the base. Shows considerable wear. Rare.
Diam. 3" (7.6 cm.)

1948.398.US America, late 19th or early 20th century.
A rectangular mold-pressed flat plaque paperweight with rounded corners, with a portrait of Abraham Lincoln pressed intaglio into the base and given an acid finish.
Length 4 1/2" (11.4 cm.); width 3" (7.6 cm.)

1948.398.G Gillinder & Sons, Philadelphia, 1876.
A centennial flat plaque impressed intaglio with a portrait of Abraham Lincoln, the portrait medallion and gavel-cut edge given an acid finish. The weight is broken and has been mended.
Diam. 3 3/16" (8.1 cm.)

1965.354.U Undetermined origin, perhaps Bohemia, 2nd half 19th century.
Three sulphide cherubs in clear glass within a circle of green canes, the lower half undercut with six fan-shaped facets, the lower sides cut with four horizontal lines, the hexagonal base scored with diamonds.
Diam. 2 15/16" (7.4 cm.)

1965.464.U Undetermined origin, late 19th or early 20th century.
A large sulphide rooster on a translucent forest green over white ground. Concave base. Glass light in weight.
Diam. 2 15/16" (7.4 cm.)

1939.46.U Undetermined origin, perhaps European, late 19th or early 20th century.
Marble enclosing sulphide dog.
Diam. 1 1/2" (3.8 cm.)

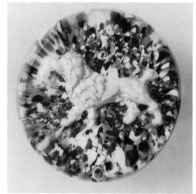

1965.469.U probably European, perhaps Belgium.
A crude but appealing sulphide French poodle on a colored chip ground. Low crown reground. Concave base.
Diam. 2 3/4" (7 cm.)

1965.351.CZ Czechoslovakia, 1918–38, or perhaps later.
A Czech weight showing a three-dimensional sulphide lion on a rich vermilion hassock surrounded by hooked festoons in lemon yellow, the weight carefully gem-faceted. Flat base shows little wear.
Height 3 7/8" (9.9 cm.); diam. 4 1/8" (10.5 cm.)

1965.352.CZ Czechoslovakia, 1918–38.
Ovoid-domed weight with three-dimensional sulphide of rooster on mottled colored-chip cushion.
Height 3" (7.6 cm.); diam. 2 3/4" (7 cm.)

1965.506.CZ Czechoslovakia, 1918–38 or later.
Sulphide stag on a hassock-shaped, mottled-pink ground surrounded by looped or hooked waves of cadmium red, the weight gem-cut with flat facets. Flat base showing little wear.
Height 3 1/2" (8.9 cm.); diam. 3" (7.6 cm.)

1939.68.M America, Whitall Tatum Co., Millville, N.J., c. 1900.
A Millville "lily" made with a crimp, the white form speckled with fused colored chips and enclosing a central bubble. The dome is footed and cut on top with a single punty. Extensive annealing crack.
Height 3 7/16" (8.8 cm.); diam. 3" (7.6 cm.)

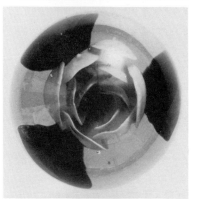

1965.86.M America, Whitall Tatum Co., Millville, N.J., c. 1900–12.
A good rose in opaque wax pink with precisely shaped dark green leaves in a sphere of glass. Pontil ground out. Flat basal rim shows normal wear.
Diam. 3 1/2" (8.9 cm.)

1962.47.US America, c. 1920–30.
A cushion of white glass spattered with emerald green and pierced by a bubble. Glass very swirly, even on surface. Base shows pontil mark and faked wear.
Diam. 2 3/4" (7 cm.)

1965.634.M America, probably Millville, N.J., c. 1900–10.
A Millville-type crimped rose in wax pink with dark green leaves in a spherical dome with footed base. Base shows pontil mark.
Diam. 3 3/16″ (8.1 cm.)

1965.379.US America, probably midwestern, late 19th or early 20th century.
A white flower made with a crimp on a swirling ground of fused, colored chips including goldstone. Base shows pontil mark and heavy wear.
Diam. 3 1/2″ (8.9 cm.)

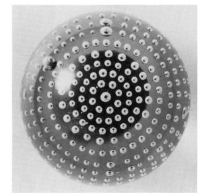

1939.62.US America, Ford City, Pa., c. 1894.
Lily form of white and colored chips with large central bubble. Flat, acid-finished base. Label on base reads "made at Ford City, Pa. 40 years ago by W. T. Carson 1934."
Diam. 3 1/2″ (8.9 cm.)

1939.75.US(?) Perhaps American, c. 1900.
Three tiers in lily form of colored chips in almost fluorescent colors, the central cross shape growing from a large bubble. Glass greasy to the touch. Base shows considerable wear and pontil mark.
Diam. 2 7/8″ (7.3 cm.)

1962.48.US America, Pilgrim Glass Corp., Ceredo, West Virginia, c. 1950–62.
Dome of uniformly spaced bubbles over smaller dome of thalo blue. Flat base. Glass yellowish.
Diam. 2 7/8″ (7.3 cm.)

1939.49. US America, early 20th century.
Crude lily form of white, pale yellow, pink, and deep emerald chips punctuated with six elongated bubbles. The polished, disproportionately narrow base (7/8″) suggests that this may once have been the top of a mantel ornament.
Diam. 2 1/2″ (6.3 cm.)

1939.91. US America, South Jersey or midwestern, early 20th century.
Lily form in white glass punctuated with bubbles and speckled with colored chips. Dome flattened at center. Base shows pontil mark.
Diam. 2 3/4″ (7 cm.)

1939.42. US America, probably midwestern, 20th century.
A lilylike flower of five thin white petals centered on a vertical bubble surrounded by five trumpet-shaped formations in blue, pink, white. Flat base shows little wear.
Diam. 2 15/16″ (7.4 cm.)

1939.18. US America, possibly West Virginia or midwestern, early 20th century.
Mantel ornament consisting of an egg-shaped weight on baluster stem, the weight containing five lily shapes centered by elongated bubbles. Glass is clear and brilliant; base shows some wear.
Height 5 7/8″ (14.9 cm.)

1939.16.US America, probably West Virginia, Ohio, or Indiana, c. 1939.
An elaborate two-tiered lily form of glass chips in garish, almost fluorescent colors. Base shows pontil mark. Basal rim given heavy false wear treatment.
Diam. 2 7/8" (7.3 cm.)

1965.704.US America, late 19th or early 20th century.
A finely constructed doorstop with form of red, white, and blue chips punctuated with five comet-tailed, silvery bubbles. Glass brilliant and heavy. Base shows pontil mark and basal rim has been ground flat.
Diam. 4 1/4" (10.8 cm.)

1939.81.US America, perhaps Ohio or Indiana, early 20th century.
Crude lily form of large colored glass chips centered with a large flattened bubble. Cushion stage prominent. Base shows pontil mark.
Diam. 3" (7.6 cm.)

1965.173.US America, maker unknown, 20th century.
Opaque baby blue flower and pale green leaves in Millville style, the flattened sphere with footed base. Pontil ground off. Rim shows signs of faked wear.
Diam. 3 3/8" (8.6 cm.)

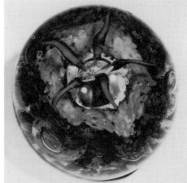

1939.66.US America, possibly by Degenhart or Gentile, 20th century.
Large weight with two-tiered orange and red lily form from which sprouts flower with large central bubble and five spidery emerald green leaves, all over a mottled chip ground. Rough base ground flat. Base paper label reads "Feb. 1, 1933. With compliments of Dr. H. C. Frankenthal."
Diam. 3 7/8" (9.9 cm.)

1965.176.US America, perhaps midwestern, 20th century.
A crude, crimped, opaque wax-pink rose and dark green leaves sit in the base of a Millville-style bottle with hollow-blown ball stopper. Flat base shows much wear, some of it perhaps faked.
Height 7 1/8″ (18.1 cm.)

1965.706.US America, New Jersey or midwestern, 20th century.
Doorstop with cobalt blue hooked trailings over red and white mottled dome pierced with elongated bubbles.
Diam. 6 1/8″ (15.5 cm.)

1939.43.US America, probably West Virginia, late 1930s.
Five pea green, five-petaled flowers over a dome of evenly spaced graduated bubbles. Flat base showing no wear.
Diam. 3 1/4″ (8.3 cm.)

1939.92.US America, probably made by Edward Rithner, Wellsburg, West Virginia, c. 1939.
Flower with six red petals edged in white rises from a translucent chip ground, base typically ground flat.
Diam. 2 5/8″ (6.7 cm.)

1965.646.U Undetermined origin, c. 1940–60.
A red over white flower with yellow center; stem and four leaves rise from a funnel-shaped grasslike ground of fused chips. The base shows almost no wear.
Diam. 3 1/8″ (7.9 cm.)

1939.52.CZ(?) Probably Czechoslovakia, 1918–38.
Tall-domed, bullet-shaped weight with four variegated colored flowers springing from a pot-shaped ground of colored chips. Flat base.
Height 3 5/16″ (8.5 cm.); diam. 2 5/8″ (6.7 cm.)

1939.37.CZ Czechoslovakia, 1918–38.
Tall-domed flower weight, the multicolored fronds rising from a white powdered ground bordered with pink and blue canes. Shows pontil mark and is atypically unfaceted. Glass bubbly.
Diam. 3 1/4″ (8.3 cm.)

1939.64.CZ Czechoslovakia, 1918–38.
A flat-bottomed weight with five red, blue, and mauve striped, trumpet-shaped flowers rising from a colored chip pot, the dome jewel-faceted in the Czech manner.
Height 2 3/4″ (7 cm.); diam. 3 1/4″ (8.3 cm.)

1939.36.CZ Probably Czechoslovakia, 1918–38.
Red flowers sprout from a flattened cushion of stridently colored fragments. Tall dome and flat base.
Diam. 3 1/16″ (7.8 cm.)

1939.88.CH China, 20th century, before 1939, but still being made.
A pair of small yellow birds perched on a red tree growing from green grass is enclosed in a hexagonal block with flat top and base, the base incised "China."
Diam. 1 1/2″ (3.8 cm.)

1939.71.CH China, 1930s.
Truncated hexagonal obelisk with latticinio hourglass form enclosing translucent green bubbles. Greasy glass. Flat base.
Height 1 7/8″ (4.7 cm.); base diam. 1 3/4″ (4.4 cm.)

1939.24.CH China, 1930s.
Hexagonal barrel-shaped form enclosing a latticinio hourglass in turn enclosing two translucent green bubbles. Greasy glass. Flat base.
Height 1 3/4″ (4.4 cm.)

1939.56.CH China, 1930s.
Cube-shaped weight with daisylike flower of red-spotted white petals rests in a matrix of translucent mulberry glass flanked by elongated bubbles. Pontil ground flat.
1 3/8″ cube (3.5 cm.)

1939.70.B. France, Baccarat, 1848–78.
Rock weight with free-form inclusion of unfused silica speckled with translucent green glass. Penned on base is "1865 this paper weight belonged to Miori Adams. Given to Carrie E. Orvis his niece in 1890—Now the property of Arthur E. Orvis. 1932." Diam. 2 5/8" (6.7 cm.)

1939.96.B France, Baccarat, 3rd quarter 19th century.
Rock weight containing random formation of unfused silica and powdered green glass. Badly bruised.
Diam. 2 1/8" (5.4 cm.)

1939.51.U Possibly France or perhaps an offhand piece from Tiffany or Steuben, early 20th century.
Pulled undersea or forest floor formations in browns and green flecked with mica fill this peak-domed, concave-based weight. The glass is exceptionally clear and heavy.
Height 2 5/8" (6.7 cm.); diam. 2 7/8" (7.3 cm.)

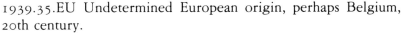

1939.35.EU Undetermined European origin, perhaps Belgium, 20th century.
A late design featuring sixteen spaced bubbles above a multicolored chip ground. Base shows pontil mark but little wear.
Diam. 3 3/16" (8.1 cm.)

1939.44.U Midwestern or possibly Belgian or German, late 19th or early 20th century.
Ground of colored chips pierced by five bubbles. High dome. Flat base.
Diam. 2 3/8" (6 cm.)

1939.90.EU Europe, possibly Belgian, late 19th or early 20th century.
Ten evenly spaced bubbles indent a mottled ground that includes chips of goldstone. Glass is faceted below the waist in Saint-Louis manner. Concave base.
Diam. 3″ (7.6 cm.)

1939.34.E England, bottle factory, 20th century.
A bottle green weight with a design of bubbles. Pontil ground away and base deeply concave with sharp rim. Little sign of wear.
Diam. 3 1/16″ (7.8 cm.)

1939.65.US America, possibly midwestern, late 19th century.
Motto weight, *Home Sweet Home,* with steel-die picture of house with tree and pump, duck floating in a foreground pond. Yellowish, badly chipped glass. Pontil mark on base.
Diam. 3″ (7.6 cm.)

1939.21.US America, probably West Virginia or midwestern, 20th century.
A masonic weight, the design in white on a translucent cobalt ground showing masonic emblem encircled by the words "M.W. Kraft Lodge 852 E. St. Louis Ill." Base shows pontil mark and large gather area.
Diam. 3 1/8″ (7.9 cm.)

1939.31.US America, possibly by Edward Rithner, c. 1939.
Motto weight, *Good Luck,* with horseshoe and flowers in white above a crude lily form of colored chips. Base ground flat.
Diam. 3 1/2″ (8.9 cm.)

1939.73.US America, West Virginia, Pennsylvania, or Ohio, early 20th century, perhaps by Henry or Edward Rithner.
A presentation weight with steel-die design of flying bird with message in its beak; flowers and leaves and the name A. S. Barton over a speckled chip ground. Pontil mark on base. Some wear.
Diam. 3 1/4″ (8.3 cm.)

1943.111.US America, Philadelphia, c. 1930.
Presentation weight reading "Ruly Vandegrift, Philadelphia, Pa." in blue ink on white wafer, all supported on a lily form in spattered pink and yellow.
Diam. 4 1/8″ (10.5 cm.)

1939.32.U Undetermined origin, perhaps American, West Virginia or midwestern, c. 1939.
A butterfly with yellow antennae, deep ruby wings edged in blue and spotted with bright canes, hovers over a dome of colored glass chips and silica grains. Flat base shows no wear at all.
Diam. 3 3/16″ (8.1 cm.)

1939.23.CH China, c. 1920 or later.
Oval weight with fish pine needles and blossoms painted with heat resistant inks in black and green on a white ground.
Length 2 5/8″ (6.7 cm.); width 2 1/4″ (5.7 cm.)

1939.28.CH China, 1930s.
Paperweight with flattened top and white ground on which is inscribed in black ink a poem by Che Chung, which roughly reads:

> The sky is cloudy, the rain falls;
> Can't cross the stream,
> The monk holding umbrella,
> On a summer day.

Diam. 2 3/16″ (5.6 cm.)

1939.93.AU(?) Europe, probably Austria, 1908.
Commemorative weight with portrait of Emperor Franz Joseph of Austria enclosed by a wreath and the inscription "1848.60.1908" enameled on the low-domed surface. Franz Joseph became emperor in 1848 and celebrated his sixtieth anniversary in 1908.
Diam. 3 1/8" (7.9 cm.)

1939.59.U Unidentified origin.
Oval clear glass with small basal foot, a paper aquatint of two ladies and a dog glued to the base.
Length 2 1/2" (6.3 cm.)

1939.17.U Possibly American, 20th century.
A clear glass egg shape flattened in one place to make it a paperweight. Surface slightly iridescent. Pontil has been ground off one end.
Length 2 5/8" (6.7 cm.)

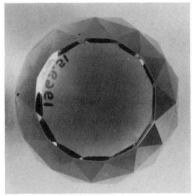

1969.51.U Undetermined origin, early 20th century.
A gem-faceted, barrel-shaped clear glass weight. Flat base and top.
Gift of Mrs. Thomas S. Da Ponte, November 24, 1969.
Diam. 2 1/2" (6.3 cm.)

1939.39.US(?) Possibly America, early 20th century.
A clear glass dome cut in typical gem style. Flat base shows typical wear.
Diam. 2 1/16" (5.2 cm.)

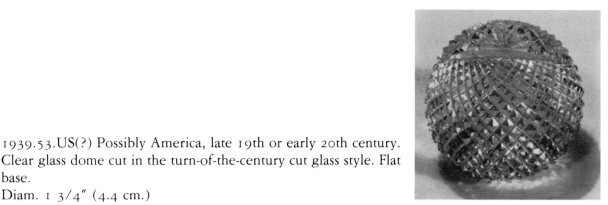

1939.53.US(?) Possibly America, late 19th or early 20th century. Clear glass dome cut in the turn-of-the-century cut glass style. Flat base.
Diam. 1 3/4″ (4.4 cm.)

1939.29.U Undetermined origin.
A hexagonal pyramid with a circular design deeply engraved into the flat base showing traces of dark red stain in the interstices.
Height 3″ (7.6 cm.); base diam. 2 1/2″ (6.3 cm.)

1939.25.U Source undetermined.
Solid "trick" glass simulating water with a sprig of artificial thistle stuck in as if resting in a vase.
Height 2 1/2″ (6.3 cm.)

1939.22.U Origin unknown, possibly Japanese, c. 1930–40.
A blown, clear glass ovoid with hollow finial and conical foot containing a lampwork opaque red fish attached to an amber trunk and branches, the tiny vessel filled with a colorless liquid.
Height 3 1/8″ (7.9 cm.)

Glossary

ANNEALING CRACK. Crack, or fissure, due to improper cooling of the glass.

ANNEALING OVEN (LEHR). Long heated chamber through which glass passes slowly on a belt from the hot end to the cool end, thus cooling the glass evenly to prevent its breaking.

ARROW. Small three-pronged motif found in rods from many sources. Also called CROW'S-FOOT.

AVENTURINE. Gold, green, or red glass combined with crystals of gold (15th century) or copper (17th century), giving the glass a lustrous sheen. Called GOLDSTONE if yellow or brownish.

BALUSTER. Stem of vaselike or turned outline.

BASAL CONCAVITY. Shallow, bowl-shaped depression left on the bottom by the grinding away of the pontil mark.

BASAL RIM. Bottom rim in paperweight with concave base.

BASE. Bottom of paperweight; usually concave.

BASKET. 1) Funnel-shaped latticinio ground typical of Saint-Louis fruit weights. 2) Outer sheath of staves typical of Clichy. 3) Encased overlay with handle; rare in Bacchus.

BLOCK. Wooden form with hemispherical interior and handle used for imparting the domed shape to a paperweight.

BOUQUET. Concentrated arrangement of canes and/or flowers with leaves.

CAMEO. See SULPHIDE.

CANE. See MILLEFIORI CANE.

CARPET GROUND. Ground composed of canes, usually of one design and color scheme.

CASED GLASS. See OVERLAY.

CHAPLET BEAD TWIST. A spiral twist of latticinio threads or strands.

CHECKER (CHEQUER). Checkerboard pattern created by spaced millefiori canes separated by a grid of white or colored filigree canes.

CLOSE MILLEFIORI. Closely compacted overall arrangement of canes, usually of great variety. Any weight with such an arrangement. See MILLEFIORI.

CLOVER CUT. Concave surface cut resembling a four-leaf clover; a specialty of the New England Glass Co.

COIL. See TORSADE.

COLOR GROUND. Translucent or opaque-colored glass background on or in which a paper-weight design rests.

CONCENTRIC. Common paperweight design in which a single cane or group of canes forms the axis for two or more concentric circles of canes.

COOKIE BASE. Thick, circular glass pad forming the base for New England Glass Co. blown fruits. Also called PAD BASE.

CRACK OFF. To break the glass object off the pontil rod.

CRIMP. Metal mold with handle used to form three-dimensional flowers.

CRIMPED CANE. Vertically ribbed or corrugated cane.

CROWN. Domed upper half of a paperweight.

CROWN WEIGHT. Hollow-blown paperweight whose walls enclose a design of vertical twisted ribbons alternating with filigree and radiating from a central cane.

CROW'S-FOOT. See ARROW.

CUSHION. Cushion-shaped paperweight ground. Often blown.

DIAMOND CUT. Evenly spaced miter cuts that cross at oblique angles.

DICHROIC. Two-colored.

DOME. Refers generally to the shape of a weight, particularly that part above the motif.

DOUBLE OVERLAY. See OVERLAY.

ENCASED OVERLAY. A single or double overlaid paperweight that has been cut with punties before being further encased in a thick coating of clear glass.

FACET. Decorative, plane-cut surface with three or more sides, used to enhance the domed surface of a paperweight. Also loosely refers to concave punty cutting.

FACETING. Flat cutting of the domed surface of a paperweight. Also, loosely, any surface cutting.

FILIGREE. Any cane or rod composed of straight or spirally twisted white or colored threads. Also loosely called MUSLIN or LACE.

FIRE-POLISH. To give the paperweight dome a final shiny, smooth surface by reheating it briefly in the fire of the glass oven, which melts the surface.

FLASH. A thin coating of colored glass applied to the crown as an overlay, or applied to the base as a ground color. Scratches and rubs off easily.

FLUTE. An incised groove of curved contour with tapering ends.

FOOT. A glass ring, flange, or pad forming the base of a weight.

GAFFER. Master glassblower, head of a team of three or four glassworkers generally referred to as a shop, "chair," or team.

GATHER. Blob of glass picked up or "gathered" by dipping the pontil iron into the molten glass batch in the glass pot. The gather may become the nucleus of the paperweight.

GAUZE. Synonym for MUSLIN, LACE, FILIGREE.

GEM-FACETED. Cut as gems are cut, with many small facets.

GOLDSTONE. Gold or yellow aventurine. See AVENTURINE.

GRASS CANE. See MOSS CANE.

GROUND. Colored background above, against, or into which the cane, flower, or sulphide design is set.

HAND COOLER. Egg-shaped glass object, solid or hollow-blown and containing a design composed of millefiori canes, filigree rods, or an upright bouquet. Intended to cool a lady's hand.

INCRUSTED. A sulphide enclosed in glass is said to be incrusted.

INTAGLIO. Incised cutting of a design into the surface of the glass. Reverse of cameo relief.

JASPER GROUND. Mottled ground composed of small glass particles, usually in two colors.

KNOP. A bulbous protuberance found in the stems of some pedestal paperweights.

LACE. See FILIGREE.

LAMPWORK. Process by which flora, fauna, and other non-millefiori design elements are formed and assembled by means of a torch.

LATTICINIO. Opaque white or colored glass appearing as threads or tapes in parallel, swirl, latticed, or spiral arrangements for use as paperweight grounds, torsades, or other decorative features.

MAGNUM. Any paperweight over 3 1/4 inches in diameter.

MANTEL ORNAMENT. Globular paperweight fused to or resting free on pedestal consisting of knopped or baluster stem, and base. Frequently seen in pairs.

MARBRIE. Paperweight design of colored festoons about a central cane or flower.

MILLEFIORI. Nineteenth-century coinage combining the Italian words *mille* (thousand) and *fiori* (flowers), describing the effect of many canes seen in proximity. A millefiori cane or any paperweight containing an arrangement of millefiori canes.

MILLEFIORI CANE. A composite colored glass rod whose cross section reveals a design. Millefiori canes are cross-sectioned for insertion in paperweights.

MINIATURE. Any paperweight up to two inches in diameter.

MOSS CANE. Green cane composed of green rods, sometimes centered by a white rod. Also called GRASS CANE.

MOSS GROUND. Ground composed of green moss canes.

MOTIF. Main design inside a paperweight.

MUSHROOM. Three-dimensional paperweight motif with a sheaf of close or concentric millefiori canes, narrow at the base and spreading as it rises into the crown. Also called TUFT.

MUSLIN. See FILIGREE.

OPALINE. White opalescent glass.

OVERLAY.   SINGLE OVERLAY. A coating of glass of one color over glass of another color. DOUBLE OVERLAY. Two coatings of differently colored glass over clear glass or glass of another color.

PAD BASE. See COOKIE BASE.

PANEL CUT. Flat narrow cut usually on the sides of a paperweight.

PANELED. Said of a weight whose internal design is divided into sections, each section composed of an enclosure of identical canes.

PATTERNED MILLEFIORI. Any planned millefiori design, as opposed to close or SCRAMBLED MILLEFIORI.

PEDESTAL WEIGHT. Refers to a prominently footed paperweight, or one with stem and foot.

PETAL CUT. Basal intaglio cutting of circular patera with alternating rays and tapered flutes.

PINCHBECK. Continental paperweight featuring a metal leaf simulating gold or silver, worked in relief by repoussé technique, and fixed in a metal or leather cap to a clear glass crown.

PONTIL MARK. Rough mark left when the paperweight is broken or cracked off the pontil rod.

PONTIL ROD or PUNTY ROD. Long iron rod used to hold a paperweight while it is being made.

PROFILE. Side elevation of a weight; often a clue to provenance.

PUNTY. Concave cut on the surface of a paperweight.

QUATREFOIL. Four-lobed or looped garland of canes.

REGROUND. Reshaped by grinding where bruises, scratches, other accidents, or wear and tear have broken the one smooth surface of the paperweight. Paperweights are shaped with a block and fire-polished when finished but still hot, but are not abrasively polished because there is no need.

REPOUSSÉ TECHNIQUE. Formation of a pattern in relief by beating up from the reverse side. See PINCHBECK.

RIBBON. Flattened band of white glass cased or overlaid with one or more colors. Usually seen twisted in crown paperweights, and as a torsade in floral paperweights.

RING. Circle of canes. Also called a ROW.

ROCK GROUND. Rough, irregular, sandy ground, composed of several elements, possibly including unfused sand, pulverized sulphide, mica, nacreous fragments, and green glass resembling algae.

ROD. Long, thin solid cylinder of clear or colored glass.

ROW (RING). Circle of canes.

SALIVA. Unwanted string or concentration of small bubbles.

SCRAMBLED PAPERWEIGHT. Random, jumbled assemblage of bits of cane, filigree, and glass chips within a matrix of clear glass to form a paperweight.

SHOT CUP. Narrow, vase-shaped bowl for holding the buckshot that held quill pens, fused to a paperweight base.

SILHOUETTE CANE (FIGURE CANE). A cane showing in cross section a human, animal, or flower silhouette.

SODDEN SNOW. Describes the appearance of white glass used as a ground in some Bacchus weights.

SPACED MILLEFIORI. Millefiori design in which the canes are set apart at more or less regular intervals.

SPOKE WEIGHT. Paperweight whose design suggests a wheel of spokes.

STAR CUT. Many-pointed star cut into base of a weight.

STAVE. Flattened, usually opaque cane used as a sheath or basket to contain other canes. See BASKET.

STRIAE. Cords or veins visible in the glass. Usually considered flaws, and resulting from improper melting of the glass batch.

SUGARY. Showing striae. See STRIAE.

SULPHIDE. Cameo relief of vitreous white clay made in a mold. Sulphides were incrusted in glass vessels, wall plaques, and paperweights.

SWIRL WEIGHT. Paperweight with rods of two or more alternating colors radiating spirally from a central cane or group of canes; a Clichy specialty.

TABLE FACET. Flat circular or other shaped cut on the top of a weight.

TAZZA. See WAFER DISH.

TORSADE. Spiral circle of ribbons, threads, or filigree rods, used to frame the motif in mushroom and upright bouquet weights, and also in early flora and fauna weights from Saint-Louis.

TRAILED. Laid on in a continuous thread.

TREFOIL. Three-lobed or looped garland of canes.

TUFT. See MUSHROOM.

"TURQUOISE." This common color designation is actually closer to cerulean blue.

UPRIGHT BOUQUET. Three-dimensional floral bouquet set vertically in a paperweight, hand cooler, stopper.

UPSET MUSLIN. Scrambled collection of filigree canes.

VISCOUS. Point beyond the softening point at which the glass is malleable and will stick to the pontil rod.

WAFER DISH. Dish supported by a stem and a foot (the foot usually in the form of a paperweight), used to hold wax seals. Also called a TAZZA.

WHITE. Opaque white.

WHORL CANE. Cane of spiral or concentric design.

WINDOW. Any round or oval, flat, or concave cut through overlay that gives a view into the interior of the weight.